●●●**POWER**
ENGINEERING
TRAINING SYSTEMS

AND

BISMARCK STATE COLLEGE

Gas Turbines and Combined Cycle

Published by PanGlobal Training Systems Ltd.
Publisher of Power Engineering Training Systems Products

Edition 1.0 May 2006

Address all inquiries to:
PanGlobal Training Systems
1301 – 16 Ave. NW, Calgary, AB Canada T2M 0L4
Attention: Director of Operations

This curriculum is endorsed by Bismarck State College.
This curriculum is endorsed by the American Boiler Manufacturers Association (ABMA).

First Printing – May 2006

ISNB13: 978-1-897251-80-5

Please visit our website for information on this and other products www.powerengineering.net

Any technical or editorial errors may be reported by e-mailing information to corrections@powerengineering.net or faxing suggested corrections to 1-403-284-8863

1301 16th Ave. NW
Calgary, Alberta
T2M 0L4

Gas Turbines and Combined Cycle

Table of Contents

UNIT 1

Industrial Gas Turbines

Here is what you will be able to do when you complete each objective:

1. Explain how power is developed in a gas turbine.

2. Describe a typical energy profile through a simple gas turbine.

3. State the advantages and disadvantages of gas turbines.

4. Describe the designs and operation of the three main components of a gas turbine, the compressor, combustor and turbine.

5. Describe the auxiliary components and systems on a gas turbine.

6. Explain the control, monitoring and protection requirements for a gas turbine.

7. Describe the main steps in a typical gas turbine start-up sequence.

INTRODUCTION

Most people are intrigued by those relatively small, round engines that hang from the wings of a large airliner and produce the amazing thrust that propels it through the air. We typically refer to them as jet engines. While a simple form of this engine was first developed as early as 1905, it's breakthrough came after World War II and since then it has been widely developed and used as propulsion for military and commercial aircraft and for the development of mechanical power in industry.

Another, more technically accurate and common name for this engine is **gas turbine**. Industrial, stationary use of this engine design has become very popular, particularly for the driving of electrical power generators. The design is very similar to that of an aircraft engine, except that the components that convert the power of the aircraft engine into thrust are replaced with components that convert the engine power into rotational power.

Gas turbines are designed and built in a wide variety of sizes and configurations. This module, however, is only intended to introduce the student to the basic theory and design that can later be applied to an understanding of the more complicated models.

What is a Gas Turbine ?

In terms of energy, a gas turbine is a device that converts the chemical energy of a fuel into mechanical energy. It could be called an internal combustion, rotary engine that attempts to combine the simplicity of the steam turbine with the advantages of internal combustion, such as in the diesel engine.

The gas turbine operates under the same basic principles as any combustion engine, where air is drawn into a combustion chamber, fuel is introduced and ignited, the products of combustion expand to do work, and then the combustion gases are exhausted from the engine. The major difference with a gas turbine, however, is that this process occurs on a continuous basis, compared to a reciprocating engine where the process repeats itself in rapid succession.

The major components of the gas turbine are a compressor, a combustor, and a turbine. In the simple machine, the compressor and the turbine are mounted at opposite ends of a single rotating shaft, with the combustor located between them.

Figure 1 shows the arrangement which operates as follows. The compressor turns at high speed to continuously draw in a relatively large volume of atmospheric air, increase its pressure and force it through the combustor.

Fuel (usually natural gas or light fuel oil) is injected through nozzles into the combustor where it burns, using a portion of the available air. Hot combustion gases are produced which, together with the remaining air, approach 2000 °F.

The hot gases/air mixture then enters the turbine section where it expands through the turbine blades and produces rotational energy before being exhausted at lower pressure and temperature.

The rotational energy is transmitted through the shaft of the gas turbine to turn the compressor and the attached external load, such as an electrical generator.

FIGURE 1

Basic Gas Turbine
Arrangement

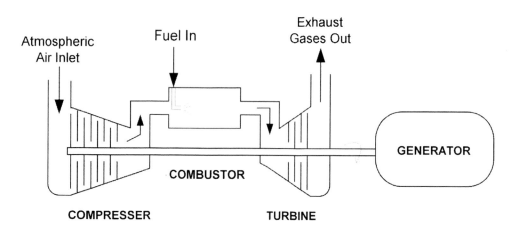

For a more graphical, detailed view, Figure 2 shows a cutaway of one design of stationary, industrial gas turbine. Note the locations of the major components.

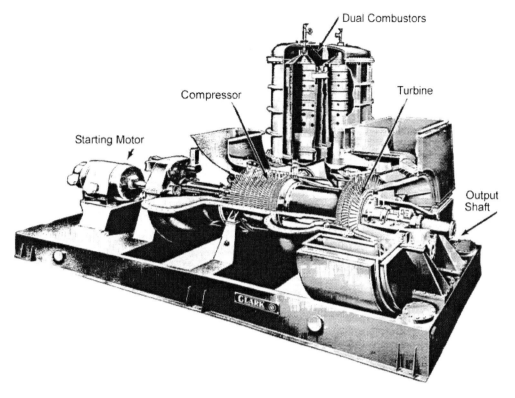

FIGURE 2

"Clark" Single-Shaft Gas Turbine

Typical Gas Turbine Profile

The energy cycle through a gas turbine can be demonstrated in simplest terms by a profile of the temperatures and pressures that occur through the engine. A profile for one unit may be as shown in Figure 3. This is not representative of all gas turbines, since many achieve a compressor discharge pressure over 400 psia (2758 kPa) The other parameters follow this profile fairly closely in most machines. The biggest difference in the power output between engines is in the compressor discharge pressure and in the size/design of the unit that determines the volume or mass of air and combustion gases that pass through it.

FIGURE 3

*Typical
Temperature/Pressure
Profile for a Gas
Turbine.*

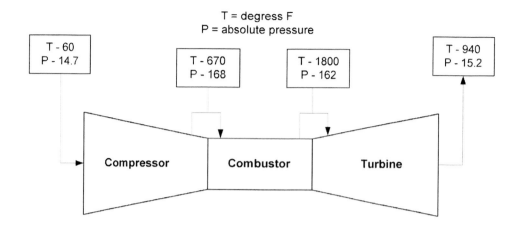

Air is drawn into the compressor at atmospheric pressure (14.7 psia/101 kPa) and temperature (60 °F/15.6 °C). In this example, the compressor increases the air pressure to 168 psia (1158 kPa) and this compression results in a temperature rise to 670 °F (355 °C).

Combustion of the fuel in the combustor further increases the temperature of the total gas mass to about 1800 °F (982 °C), which effectively converts the available chemical energy in the fuel into thermal energy in the gas.

The pressure does not increase in the combustor and the high temperature gas enters the turbine section where it expands through the blades, converting some of its thermal energy into rotational mechanical energy. Expansion produces a pressure drop that results in near atmospheric pressure at the outlet of the turbine, plus a noticeable temperature drop to 940 °F (504 °C).

Note that the energy loss from the turbine is basically the energy that was required to heat the air and fuel from their inlet temperatures up to the final exhaust temperature. Many installations, such as Cogeneration facilities, improve overall system efficiency by using this large amount of exhaust heat in downstream processes to produce steam or for other heating purposes.

Advantages and Disadvantages of Gas Turbines

When compared to conventional steam plant/steam turbine systems or to other combustion engine drivers, the gas turbine has several advantages.

1. Cooling water requirements are low compared to a condensing steam plant. The turbine itself requires no cooling water.

2. The absence of reciprocating parts contributes to lower maintenance costs and longer life. The gas turbine is comparatively simple in design.

3. The gas turbine can run virtually unattended, incorporating remote and automatic controls.

4. It has a high power-to-weight ratio. That is, for its compactness it can deliver more power than much larger installations.

5. It has rapid start-up capabilities.

However, there are also some significant disadvantages.

1. The thermal efficiency is lower than that of a steam turbine plant, although this can be compensated for by using the exhaust heat for process or heating purposes.

2. Only light, clean burning fuels can be used.

3. Gas turbines tend to be much noisier than other prime movers, due to their high rotational speeds.

GAS TURBINE MAJOR COMPONENTS

The major components of the gas turbine, as mentioned, are the compressor, combustor(s) and turbine.

Compressor

The purpose of the compressor is to draw free air in, pressurize it, then deliver it into the combustor(s). The pressure energy of the air that is created by the compressor is then available to produce work by expanding back to atmospheric pressure in the turbine. Since the compressor is mounted on the same shaft as the turbine, it receives its driving power from the turbine. About 2/3 of the turbines power output is normally required to drive the compressor.

There are two dynamic compressor designs commonly used in gas turbine; these are the radial and the axial.

The **radial compressor**, also called a **centrifugal compressor**, consists of one or more impellers mounted on the shaft and surrounded by a casing which contains a number of diffuser vanes. The principle of the radial compressor is that, as it rotates at high speed, air is drawn into the center, or hub, of the impeller. Centrifugal action then forces the air radially outwards at increased velocity and pressure into the diffuser vanes where, due to the diverging shape of the vanes, the velocity drops and the energy is converted into further pressure. A discharge channel carries the air to the combustor(s). When more than one impeller is used, the discharge from the first enters the hub of the following impeller so that the pressure is increased in stages. Rarely are more than two impellers used in a gas turbine.

Figure 4 (a) shows the impeller and diffuser arrangement.
Figure 4 (b) shows a typical impeller.

FIGURE 4 (a) and (b)

Typical Centrifugal
Compressor Impeller

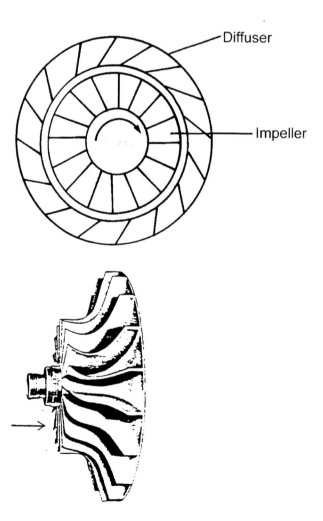

Diffuser

Impeller

Figure 5 shows one design of gas turbine that uses a two-stage centrifugal compressor.

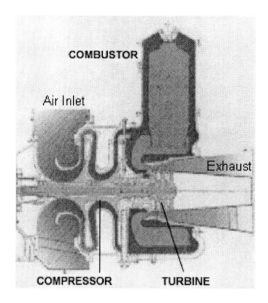

FIGURE 5

Gas Turbine with Two-Stage Centrifugal Compressor

The **axial compressor** produces flow that is parallel to the axis, or shaft, of the compressor. It consists of a number of stages of alternate rotating and stationary curved blades which force the air through a casing that gets gradually smaller in cross-sectional area. As the compressor spins at high speed each set of rotating blades forces the air back through the following stationary blades which reduce the velocity and increase the pressure of the air. The pressure gradually increases as the air passes through the compressor stages until it reaches the combustor.

Figure 6 shows a simple sketch of the axial compressor arrangement.
Also, refer back to Figure 2 for an example of an axial compressor gas turbine.

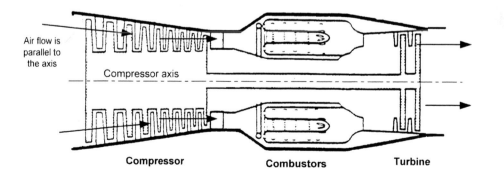

FIGURE 6

Axial Compressor discharging into combustors

Combustor(s)

The purpose of the combustor(s) is to burn fuel to dramatically increase the temperature of the compressed air before it enters the turbine section. While combustor sizes and details vary, the general design is that of a cylindrical "can" with an outer shell that receives the air flow and an inner shell that contains the combustion chamber. A fuel injection nozzle is fitted in one end of the combustor, along with a spark igniter.

The air from the compressor, at pressures up to 450 psi. (3102 kPa), enters the outer shell and flows through holes into the combustion chamber where it mixes with the vaporized fuel from the nozzle. This design preheats the air before combustion and also cools the combustor shell. Some air may be injected at the end near the fuel nozzle for better mixing and more efficient combustion. On start-up, when initial ignition is established, the ignitor de-energizes and combustion is continuous after that. Approximately 1/3 of the total air that flows from the compressor is consumed in the combustion process.

FIGURE 7 (a) and (b)

Combustor design and multiple burner arrangement

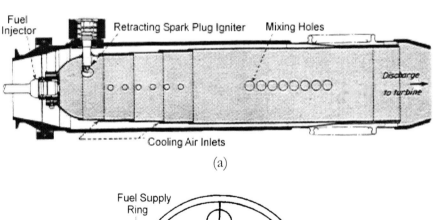

(a)

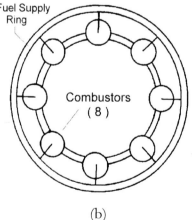

(b)

Some gas turbines, usually of smaller capacity, have single or dual combustors mounted vertically, external to the turbine casing (see Figures 2 and 5 for examples). Others have several horizontal combustors, mounted within the casing and encircling the turbine. Figure 7(b) shows an example of this arrangement with eight combustors supplied from a common fuel ring. Figure 8 shows how this design fits in a turbine casing.

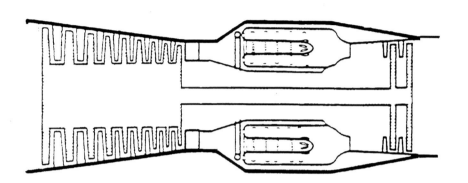

FIGURE 8

Internal, multiple combustor design

Turbine

The purpose of the turbine section is to absorb energy from the hot, expanding gases from the combustor(s) and to convert this into mechanical energy that turns the turbine shaft, producing work in the compressor and/or in an external load, such as a generator. Gas turbines employ an axial flow turbine, similar in design to the axial compressor. The hot gases pass through a series of stages, each consisting of a row of stationary nozzle blades (mounted to the casing) followed by rotating blades (mounted on discs on the shaft). As the gases flow through the nozzle blades, they expand and convert pressure into kinetic energy, increasing their velocity. The gases then hit the moving blades, imparting a force that creates motion and does work.

Figure 9 shows a partially dismantled turbine section. Because the gases expand toward the outlet of the turbine, the casing gets gradually larger to accommodate the increased volume and the successive stages of blading also get larger. Generally the turbine section requires only two or three stages to produce the required work output of the gas turbine.

FIGURE 9

Partially disassembled
Turbine Section

Turbines may be of the impulse or reaction type, as reflected in the blade shape and operating principle. Figure 10 demonstrates the two designs.

In the impulse design, the flow passages between rotating blades are of constant cross-sectional area, resulting in virtually no velocity, pressure or temperature change. The impulse of the gas as it hits and changes direction between the blades causes the turning motion. Velocity and pressure changes occur in the stationary nozzles only.

In the reaction design, however, both the rotating and the stationary blade passages act as nozzles to accelerate the gas flow as pressure and temperature decrease. The reaction force of the gases back onto the blades causes the rotation. Reaction designs are more efficient and are almost always the design choice for gas turbines.

Impulse Blades

Reaction Blades

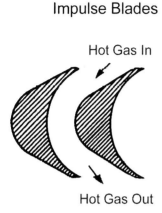

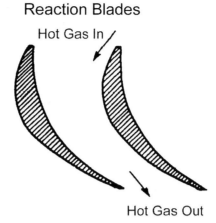

FIGURE 10

Impulse and Reaction Blade Design

FIGURE 11

Typical Reaction Blades from a turbine rotor

AUXILIARY COMPONENTS AND SYSTEMS

Several auxiliary components and systems are required to ensure a gas turbine operates safely, efficiently, and with minimum troubles. The major ones include a starting motor, turning motor, reducing gear, fuel supply, lubrication, steam/water injection, fire suppression, and water washing.

Starting Motor

Until air flow and combustor ignition are established the gas turbine cannot be self-sustaining. Therefore, a separate drive motor must be provided to turn the compressor until sufficient airflow is attained for safe ignition of the combustor(s). This starting motor may be electric or gas powered and is coupled to the shaft through the gearbox, either directly or by belt drive, using a clutching device to engage or disengage the motor.

The starting system is used only during start-up to accelerate the turbine from 0% RPM up to a self-sustaining acceleration speed (usually about 55% of operating RPM), at which point the starter disengages and the turbine continues to accelerate to 100% RPM on its own. When an electric motor is used for the starter, often it is a variable frequency motor, in which the speed can be increased in stages to accommodate a more controlled start-up.   Refer back to Figure 2 for one example of a starting motor arrangement..

Turning Motor

The turning motor is a small DC motor that turns the turbine rotor at very slow speed. Its sole purpose is to maintain a slow, steady rotation of the turbine for several hours after the unit is shut down. An engine shutdown causes the turbine to become extremely hot and this heat can cause a temperature imbalance in the turbine and a slight deflection of the rotor. If the turbine were to be restarted before it is completely cooled, this imbalance would cause excessive vibrations. Continuous slow turning during the cool-down period prevents the rotor deflection and allows the turbine to be safely restarted at any time.

Reducing Gear

Gas turbines typically rotate at speeds ranging from +/- 14,000 to 21,000 RPM. These speeds are necessary in order to achieve the desired pressures and mass flows out of the compressor. However, the loads attached to the turbine must turn at much lower speeds. Power generators, for example, must turn at only 1800 RPM (if 60 hz) or 1500 RPM (if 50 hz). To make the turbine power useful then, a speed-reducing gearbox, incorporating a complex arrangement of gears, is installed between the turbine and the generator. Besides reducing the speed of the generator shaft the gearbox may also contain other auxiliary gears that connect shaft power to oil pumps, fuel pumps and the starter motor.

Fuel Supply Systems

There are two common fuels used in the combustor(s) of industrial gas turbines. These are natural gas and light fuel oil. The combustor requires that the fuel be supplied to the burner nozzle at a controllable rate for varying load demands and at a constant, relatively high pressure for good mixing with the air. An external supply system must include the necessary shutoff valves, vents, pressure regulators, filters, and flow control valves. In the case of natural gas, a gas compressor may be required to boost the supply pressure to the combustor fuel injectors. Fuel oil will require storage and a pump to pressurize the oil for efficient atomization in the burner. Figure 12 shows a very simplified version of a fuel gas supply to the turbine.

FIGURE 12

Gas Turbine Fuel Gas Supply

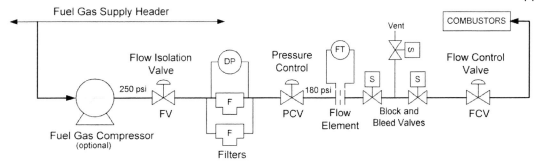

Lubrication System

The shaft of a simple gas turbine is supported by two bearings, one near each end of the shaft. These high-speed moving parts require careful, continuous lubrication whenever the shaft is in motion, to reduce friction, eliminate wear, and provide cooling. Lubrication must also be supplied to the reducing gear. The turbine employs an external, forced lubrication system consisting of **main lube oil pumps** that circulate the oil from a reservoir, through filters and a cooler, to the bearings and reducing gear. Pressure and temperature controls are built into the system to ensure operating parameters are maintained. Most systems also have an additional, smaller **pre/post lube oil pump**. Its purpose is to circulate oil to the bearings for several minutes before the turbine is started and again after the turbine is shut down, during the cool-down period. Figure 13 is a simplified lube oil system for a gas turbine.

FIGURE 13

Simplified Lube Oil System for a Gas Turbine

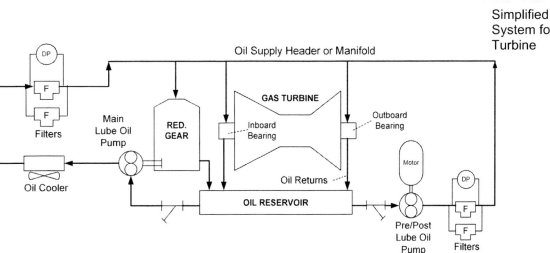

Because of the very high rotational speeds of gas turbines (up to 21,000 rpm) a special, synthetic lubricating oil must be used. This very expensive lubricant provides better stability and viscosity control and better resistance to foaming and corrosion.

Steam/Water Injection System

Many industrial gas turbines have a system that injects either steam or water into the combustor(s) during operation. The purpose is twofold. First it reduces the temperature of the burner flame so that less nitrogen oxide compounds (NOx) are created as products of combustion. NOx is an undesirable environmental pollutant which result from high temperature combustion and must be minimized at the turbine exhaust. The second purpose for steam is that it increases the mass flow through the turbine, which provides more power and increases the overall efficiency. The injection system typically consists of piping from an external high-pressure steam source, that delivers steam through isolation and flow control valves, into the combustion zone. Figure 14 shows the main components of a steam injection system

FIGURE 14

Combustor Steam Injection for a Gas Turbine

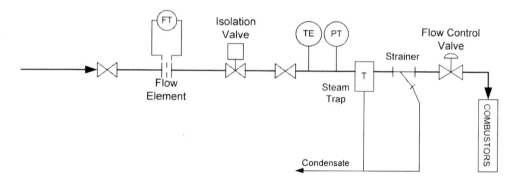

Leak Detection and Fire Suppression

Since gas turbines are very noisy, they are usually housed in a closed, ventilated enclosure. One danger of this is that any leaks in fuel lines can create a combustible atmosphere and/or a localized fire. Fire damage could be very extensive and expensive, so most units are provided with gas detectors and flame sensors, inside the enclosure. These may initiate warnings only to operating personnel or they may be set to automatically shut down the turbine and initiate fire suppression. The latter is usually a water deluge system consisting of spray heads above the unit with a supply valve that can be automatically or manually opened when fire is detected.

Water Wash System

If deposits are permitted to accumulate on the blades, the compressor will become less efficient and will have to burn more fuel for the same power output. If enough deposits occur a condition could develop that causes the compressor to **surge**. This is a potentially destructive condition in which the compressor is unable to deliver the required flow to sustain the discharge pressure, resulting in a momentary backward flow of air through the compressor. The sudden pressure change across the blades can virtually destroy the compressor if allowed to continue or if too severe.

A technique that allows the blades to be cleaned while the gas turbine is operating at 100% speed is called water washing. A cleaning solution is sprayed into the intake of the engine, through atomizing nozzles mounted in the intake plenum. The solution thoroughly wets the compressor blades, dissolves any dirt, and continues through the engine. An external supply system for the wash solution consists of a solution tank in which the cleaning solution is mixed with demineralized water, , a positive displacement pump, and a fine filter that ensures no large particles are pumped into the engine.

CONTROL, MONITORING AND PROTECTION OF GAS TURBINES

While the gas turbine is a relatively simple machine its efficiency and reliability of operation demand that it be monitored and controlled within strict parameters. It also requires protection against conditions that could damage the machine. A programmable logic control (PLC) is generally used to monitor the many parameters received from instruments mounted on the turbine and it's auxiliary systems. If any of these parameters reach unsatisfactory condition the PLC will activate alarms or will shutdown the turbine. The PLC also controls the sequencing and monitoring of the actions that must occur during a start-up, shutdown, or load change of the gas turbine.

Control

In addition to their visual inspections of external conditions, the personnel responsible for the operating of the gas turbine interact largely with the PLC through a computer-based control system. Here the operator can see all the necessary monitoring parameters for the engine and all the auxiliary systems and can initiate necessary operations, such as start-up, shutdown, water washing, load changes, etc.

Monitoring

Continuous monitoring of the gas turbine operation can typically be classified into three areas: gas path monitoring, vibration monitoring, and auxiliaries monitoring.

Gas Path Monitoring

Temperature and pressure transmitters are located at the four key points in the flow path (see Figure 3). The inlet gas temperature (**IGT**) is monitored since it provides a relative indication of the mass flow available to the compressor. Colder air is more dense that warm air. The compressor discharge pressure (**CDP**) is monitored because it is an important indication of the power that will be available in the turbine (higher pressure means more power) and it provides warning if compressor efficiency is dropping (lower CDP may mean the blades need washing). In some cases, a dangerous reduction in CDP may also be used to automatically open an auxiliary blow-off line that will prevent the compressor from going into surge. The turbine inlet temperature (**TIT**) is an indication of the heat available for conversion to work in the turbine section. Control of this temperature determines the amount of fuel that is burned in the combustor. Finally, the turbine exhaust gas temperature (**EGT**) provides useful information as to the overall efficiency of the turbine. Often, when the turbine exhausts into other equipment, such as in cogeneration, this temperature becomes more significant.

Vibration Monitoring

The extremely high rotational speed of the gas turbine requires that it be monitored very closely for vibrations that could lead to massive damage. Vibration pickups are therefore mounted at key spots along the shaft (or shafts if a multi-shaft machine) to detect any deflection. The deflections are transmitted back to the PLC where alarms or shutdowns will be activated if limits are exceeded. Vibration monitors are also mounted in reducing gears.

Auxiliary Monitoring

The three most important auxiliary systems that require monitoring are the fuel, lubrication and fire suppression systems. The main factors monitored are fuel flow and pressure to the combustors, lube oil pressure/temperature/flow to the bearings and gear box, and combustible gas, fire and smoke detection at the turbine enclosure.

Protection Systems

Gas turbine protection means alarms or shutdowns that activate when unfavourable conditions occur on the machine or its auxiliaries. Alarms generally occur first to allow the operator to take corrective action, but if the condition worsens to a potentially destructive level, then an **emergency stop** of the gas turbine will occur. Some of these stops are designed for protection of the turbine during full-speed operation. Others are used during activities, such as start-up, to protect the turbine if certain parameters are not met when required in the sequence. Following are just a few examples of conditions that may cause alarms and shutdowns. It is far from an all-inclusive list.

Alarms:	Shutdowns:
Lube Oil reservoir level Low	Lube Oil reservoir level Low-Low
Lube Oil pressure Low	Lube Oil pressure Low-Low
Lube Oil filter differential Hi	Lube Oil filter differential Hi-Hi
Starting Lube Oil pressure Low Low	Starting Lube Oil pressure Low-
Fuel Gas or Oil pressure Hi	Fuel Gas or Oil pressure Hi-Hi
Fuel Gas or Oil pressure Low	Fuel Gas or Oil pressure Low-Low
Running EGT Hi	Running EGT Hi-Hi
	Flame-Out Failure
	Overspeed Trip
Engine Shaft vibration Hi	Engine Shaft vibration Hi-Hi
Gearbox vibration Hi	Gearbox vibration Hi-Hi
Bearing temperature Hi	Bearing temperature Hi-Hi
	Excessive start cycle time
	Engine light-off failure
Steam injection pressure Hi Hi	Starter Motor failed
	Pre-post Lube Oil pump failed
	ESD Button depressed

GAS TURBINE START-UP SEQUENCE

There are very few operations that an operator physically performs on a gas turbine. Aside from preparing the auxiliary systems for operation, ensuring fuel supply and oil system are ready for service the remaining interaction is mostly through the computer monitoring system and PLC. It is good to understand what happens, however, when the operator pushes the start "button". Figure 15, is a simplified graphic of an abbreviated starting sequence of a gas turbine. While it shows the major steps, it should be realized that the actual sequence will likely involve other intermediate steps and many interlocks may need to be satisfied in order for steps to proceed. There will usually be other interlocks that relate to the load or process that the turbine supplies, such as the generator or the cogeneration facility.

FIGURE 15

Gas Turbine Start-up Sequence

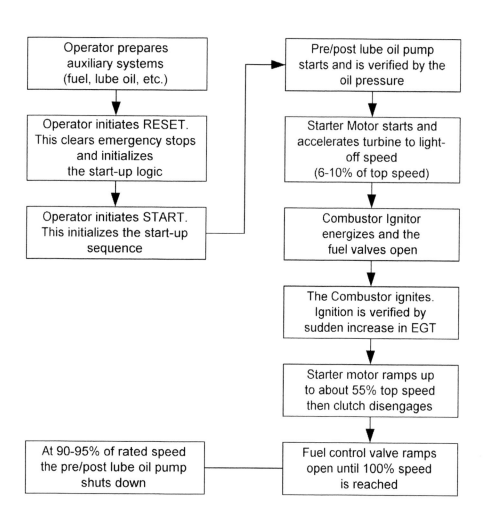

UNIT 2

Gas Turbine Principles and Designs

Here is what you will be able to do when you complete each objective:

1. Explain gas turbine advantages and disadvantages, background and industrial applications. Identify the types of gas turbines, their major components and describe the operating principles of a simple gas turbine.

2. Explain single and dual shaft arrangements for gas turbines. Describe open cycle and closed cycle operation.

3. Describe a typical open cycle gas turbine installation, including buildings or enclosures, intake and exhaust systems, auxiliary systems, and reducing gear.

4. Explain the efficiency and rating of gas turbines and describe the purpose and applications of gas turbine cycle improvements, including intercooling, regenerating, reheating and combined cycle.

5. Describe various aspects of compressor design and centrifugal and axial types of compressors.

6. Describe the types, operation, components and arrangements of combustors.

7. Describe turbine section design and operation especially with respect to blading and materials.

8. Explain the types and functions of the control systems and instrumentation needed for gas turbine operation.

9. List the typical operating parameters of a gas turbine; describe the effects of compressor inlet temperature, compressor discharge pressure, and turbine inlet temperature on gas turbine performance.

INTRODUCTION

Gas turbines are a major source of power for a variety of industrial applications. They are designed in a wide range of sizes and configurations. Their capabilities, efficiency and power output are continually being improved through design changes.

GAS TURBINE ADVANTAGES

Modern gas turbines have a number of significant advantages over other types of power plants, including:

- Capability to produce large amounts of power, currently up to 250 MW (335 million Btu)

- High power to weight ratio, making them especially suitable for applications (such as offshore) where weight must be minimized

- Ability to use a wide range of liquid and gaseous fuels

- Ability to start rapidly, which is important for backup power generation

- Relatively simple and compact design with few and simple auxiliary systems

- High availability and reliability and ability to minimize outage time by quick replacement of the gas turbine in case of major failure

- Remote operation capability with minimal operational manpower requirements

DISADVANTAGES

- The turbine engine has a few drawbacks, which have prevented its widespread use in automotive applications

- Turbine engines have high manufacturing costs - Because of the complicated design, manufacturing is expensive

- A turbine engine changes speed slowly - A gas turbine is slow to respond, relative to a reciprocating engine, to changes in throttle request
- A gas turbine is less suitable for low-power applications - At partial throttle conditions, the efficiency of the gas turbine decreases

- A turbine requires intercoolers, regenerators and/or reheaters to reach efficiencies comparable to current gasoline engines; this adds significant cost and complexity to a turbine engine

TYPES OF INDUSTRIAL GAS TURBINES

There are two basic types of industrial gas turbines: aero-derivative - derived from the jet engines used in aircraft; and heavy-duty gas turbines — only designed for land-based applications. Each type has advantages and disadvantages, which make them more suitable for certain applications. However, there is considerable overlap in their usage and there are no hard and fast application rules.

Aero-derivative gas turbines, such as the 55 MW (73.7 million Btu)General Electric LM 5000 in Fig. 1, are aircraft (jet) engines adapted for industrial use either by:

- Expanding the engine gases through an added power turbine to drive a generator or mechanical load, rather than expanding the exhaust through a jet nozzle as occurs in aircraft

- Converting a turboprop engine

FIGURE 1

Aero Derivative Gas Turbine
(Courtesy of General Electric)

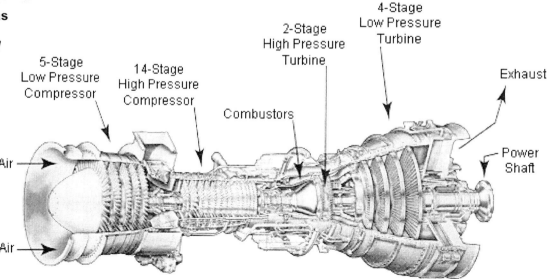

- Potentially more efficient than reciprocating engines with the same power rating (depending on the way they are integrated into the plant power system)

- Able to use either natural gas or good quality liquid fuels and sometimes designed to allow switching between them

Heavy-duty gas turbines share many design aspects with steam turbines, compressors and plant machinery. Because weight is less of an issue in many applications, their layout is more flexible and their design is more rugged than aero-derivatives.

In general, heavy-duty gas turbines are:

- Larger and heavier than their aero-derivative equivalents

- Very durable with long intervals between overhauls which makes them especially suitable for base load applications

- More efficient than aero-derivative engines of the same capacity

- Able to use all fuels including distillates, residuals and crude oil

- Able to accommodate a flexible layout between compressor, combustors and turbine to allow for inter-cooling, regeneration, steam injection, combined cycle, closed cycle and reheat

An example is the gas turbine shown in Fig. 2. The identification of the major components of the gas turbine unit, and in particular, that one of those components is referred to specifically as the turbine. The term "gas turbine" is commonly applied to the entire collection of components, including the turbine section. However, when the term "turbine" is used on its own, this refers only to the specific turbine section of the gas turbine.

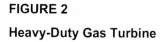

FIGURE 2

Heavy-Duty Gas Turbine

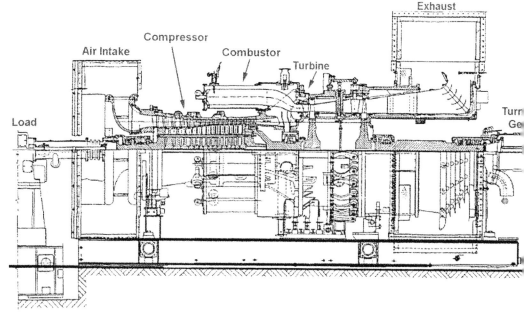

INDUSTRIAL APPLICATIONS OF GAS TURBINES

Industrial gas turbines are used for a very wide range of applications, for both electric power generation and to drive equipment such as pumps and compressors.

When gas turbines are used to generate electricity, it can be to produce either a "base load", or to provide emergency (back-up power), or to produce "peak power". Base load, as the term suggests, means that the unit produces electricity on an on-going basis, within a fairly steady demand range. Peak power, on the other hand, refers to the production of power only during those periods of the day when the overall electrical distribution network for a community (town, city, state or larger region) is close to being overloaded.

In Canada, this is typically between 4 pm and 7 pm during the winter months, when there is heavy simultaneous domestic load, such as stoves and washing machines. In such cases, large electrical producers and distributors create incentives for companies to provide some of their own power during those periods. These incentives more than compensate for the cost of the gas turbine unit.

Base load systems range from very small to plants in excess of 250 MW (335 million Btu). Fig. 3 shows a 28 kW (37 million Btu) micro turbine producing base load power. The hot exhaust gases from the gas turbine pass to the once through boiler where steam is generated at a pressure of 115 psi and is used for process work.

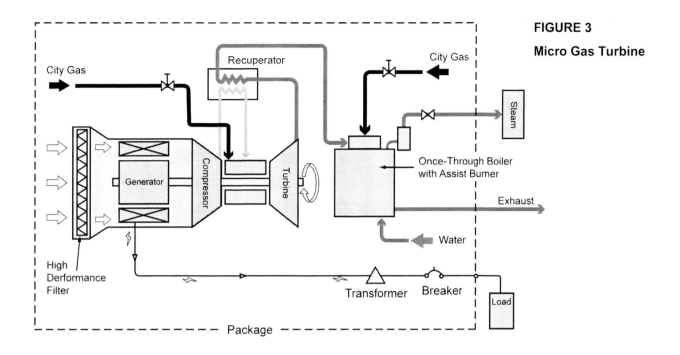

FIGURE 3

Micro Gas Turbine

GAS TURBINE MAJOR COMPONENTS

While gas turbines exist in many different designs, every gas turbine has three major components, which are shown in Fig. 3:

- Compressor section
- Combustion section, also called a combustor
- Turbine section

SIMPLE GAS TURBINE OPERATING PRINCIPLES

Referring to Fig. 4, ambient air enters the air compressor and is compressed to a pressure of 160 – 435 psi and then passes to the combustion chamber. The combustion chamber adds fuel (natural gas or oil) to some of the air from the compressor to achieve continuous combustion. This combustion causes a sudden increase in temperature to about 3600°F, which is the flame temperature. By mixing the combusted products with the remaining compressed air, the temperature is reduced to 1650°F at the exit of the combustion section to achieve a temperature low enough for the turbine materials.

The hot gases from the combustion chamber then enter the turbine. The turbine expands the air from the combustion section and produces mechanical power to drive the air compressor and a generator, which produces electricity. These gases exit the turbine at nearly atmospheric pressure, but still at a temperature of up to 1200°F.

FIGURE 4

Simple Gas Turbine

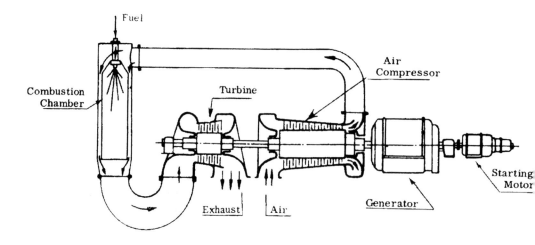

SINGLE SHAFT

In the single shaft arrangements shown in Fig. 5, the compressor, turbine and load are all connected and rotate at the same speed. The more common situation is for the load to be connected to the turbine, as shown in Fig. 5(a) and Fig. 6. Another arrangement, as shown in Fig. 5(b), is for the load to be connected to the compressor.

FIGURE 5

Single Shaft Layouts

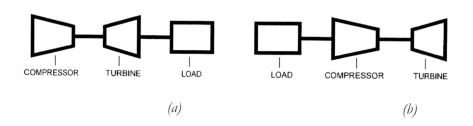

(a)   *(b)*

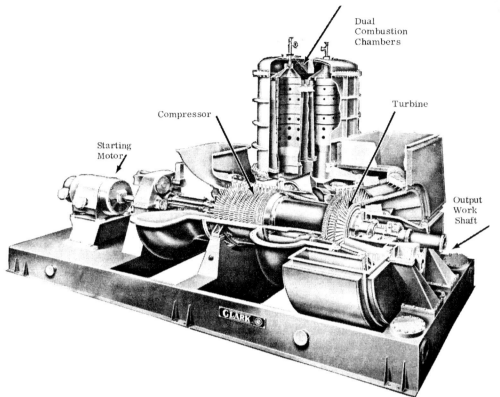

Dual
Combustion
Chambers

FIGURE 6

**Single Shaft Gas
Turbine**
(Courtesy of Clark)

DUAL SHAFT

In the dual shaft arrangement shown in Fig. 7, the compressor is driven by a high pressure turbine while the load is driven by a low pressure turbine with no mechanical linkage between the low pressure and the high pressure turbines. A single-shaft arrangement is used for power generation where a constant speed is required but is rarely used for other applications. It is mechanically simpler than a two-shaft arrangement, but requires a large starting motor. This is because, during start-up, the compressor of a gas turbine must provide a threshold air pressure for ignition in the combustor. In single shaft systems, the starting motor must turn the turbine and load mass, as well as the compressor, whereas in two-shaft arrangements, the starting motor does not have to turn the load mass along with the compressor.

The advantage of this arrangement is greater flexibility. The load may be operated at varying speeds while the compressor speed remains constant. Conversely, the load speed may be constant as in the case of a generator while the compressor speed may be varied. Another advantage of the dual shaft machine is that a smaller starting motor may be used, as during start-up it is only necessary to turn the compressor and the high-pressure turbine.

FIGURE 7

Dual Shaft Arrangement

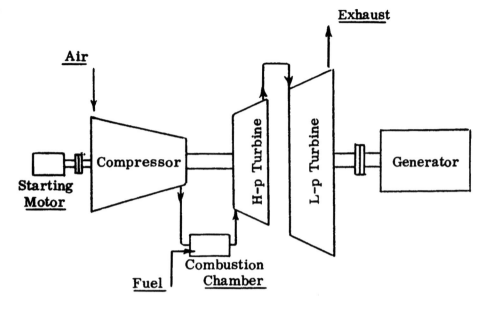

OPEN CYCLE OPERATION

An open cycle gas turbine system is shown in Fig. 8. Air is drawn into the compressor inlet from the atmosphere, compressed and supplied to the turbine after heating with oil in the combustion chamber. It then expands through the gas turbine and exhausts to atmosphere. The system is termed "open cycle" because the working fluid (air) is drawn from the atmosphere at the beginning of the cycle and returned to atmosphere at the end of the cycle. The term "simple" is used because the plant has no additional features such as heat exchangers, reheaters, intercoolers, and so on.

FIGURE 8

Simple Open-Cycle Gas Turbine System

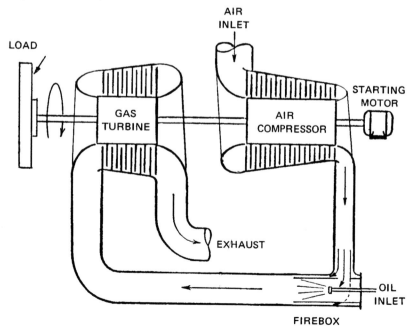

CLOSED CYCLE OPERATION

The simple, open cycle can be modified so that the working fluid is contained and re-circulated within the system, rather than being drawn in from and exhausted to the atmosphere. Atmospheric air may be, however, used in the combustor and heat exchanger to heat the re-circulating working fluid. Fig. 9 shows a closed cycle gas turbine system. Starting at the inlet of the compressor, the working fluid is pressurized, as in the open cycle, but it is then pre-heated in a regenerator by the hot exhaust gases from the turbine exhaust before its main heating process in the air heater.

The air heater is a heat exchanger in which hot combustion gases, from the burning of a fuel, transfer heat to the working fluid. The fluid then expands through the turbine. To be re-used, the hot gases at the exit of the turbine must be cooled before compression. To accomplish this, the gases give up their residual heat, first in the regenerator (where they preheat the working fluid en-route to the air heater) and then in the cooler, where they exchange heat with cooling water.

Closed cycle systems are associated with modifications whose purpose is to increase the net power output and thermal efficiency of the equipment, which is discussed more thoroughly in Objective 4. In that section, more detail will be given regarding the purpose and operation of the regenerator and air heater shown in Fig. 9.

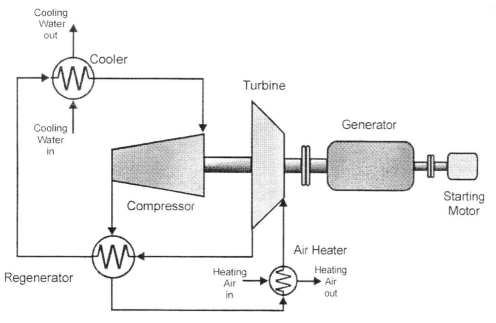

FIGURE 9

Closed Cycle Turbine System

Closed Cycle System Advantages

- Higher pressures can be used throughout the cycle and therefore higher densities of the working fluid are obtained. This increases the output of the machine for the same physical dimensions.

- The working fluid is clean, and does not cause corrosion or erosion of the turbine.

- The working fluid need not support combustion and may be chosen for its superior thermodynamic properties.

- A cheap fuel may be used.

Closed Cycle System Disadvantages

- A supply of cooling water is required.

- Heat-exchanger efficiencies are considerably lower than those of direct internal combustion.

- The complexity, size, and cost of the system have been considerably increased.

GAS TURBINE INSTALLATION

A gas turbine installation involves a number of additional components, systems and equipment that vary widely depending on the type of gas turbine, its location, environmental conditions and application. The following describes the items that are usually part of a gas turbine installation. Fig. 10 gives a comprehensive picture of most systems needed with a gas turbine.

FIGURE 10

**Overview Of Systems
For A Gas Turbine**

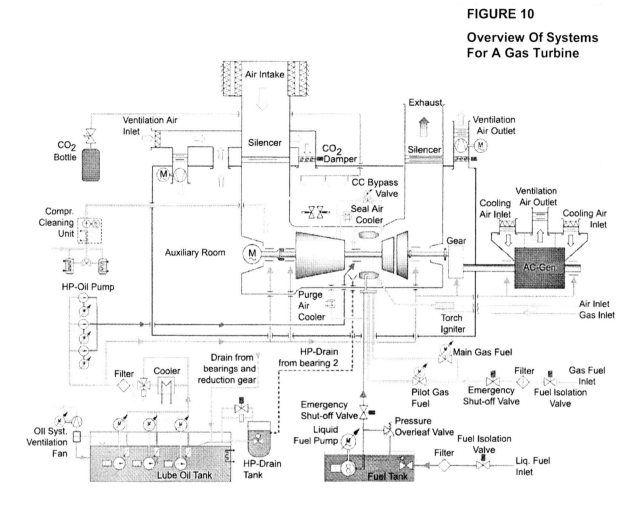

Buildings and Enclosures

Many gas turbines are contained in an enclosure that protects it from the environment, reduces noise and provides protection for personnel in case of failure. Especially in colder climates, the unit may be located in a separate building with lay-down space for maintenance. The buildings or enclosures may incorporate heat and gas detection, ventilation systems and fire suppression, such as CO_2 or Halon.

Intake and Exhaust

A gas turbine always has an air intake that filters the air to remove contaminants and prevent damage from foreign objects. The intake plenum ensures smooth flow into the gas turbine compressor section. Since cooler air is denser than warm air, some air intakes incorporate special cooling systems to decrease the air inlet temperature. This increase in air density means that more mass can flow through the turbine and therefore produce more power.

The exhaust system provides a safe exit for the hot exhaust gases and may include a silencer to reduce sound to acceptable limits. The exhaust may also flow to a waste heat recovery heat exchanger to supply heat to some other process at the overall facility. This will be discussed later in this module. Both the intake and exhaust need to operate with the lowest possible pressures losses to minimize resultant losses in power and efficiency.

Auxiliary Systems

A number of auxiliary systems are needed to support the operation of the gas turbine, including:

- A fuel gas system to ensure that fuel is provided to the combustion section at the proper temperature and pressure

- Fuel treatment systems to clean and treat fuels, if required

- A lube oil system for the lubrication of bearings

- A hydraulic oil system for the operation of the fuel valves

- A steam injection system to reduce emissions and/or increase output, if required

- Anti-icing systems, which provide heat to the air intake to eliminate the buildup of ice in very cold climates

Reducing Gears

For many applications, it is necessary to reduce the speed of the power turbine to match that of the load equipment. This is especially true for gas turbines that drive generators, which need to run at a constant speed, usually 1800/3600 r/min for 60 Hz generators and 1500/3000 r/min for 50 Hz.

EFFICIENCY AND RATING OF GAS TURBINES

Gas turbines are normally rated in terms of the power produced at the output shaft where it connects to the generator or compressor. The power rating specified by the manufacturer will be in kilowatts or horsepower, at a standard of 60°F and at sea level, using natural gas as a fuel, air with 60% humidity and with no intake or exhaust losses.

Thermal efficiency is the ratio in % of the rated power and the fuel energy rate. The fuel energy rate is calculated by multiplying the fuel flow rate by the lower heating value of the fuel. Modern gas turbines are able to reach efficiencies of 35% to 40% in simple cycle mode without the cycle improvements or combined cycle described below.

CYCLE IMPROVEMENTS

In order to improve the efficiency of the basic gas turbine cycle, three methods, or a combination of them, can be implemented. As simple cycle gas turbines are improving in efficiency, these cycle improvements are becoming less necessary as combined cycle, utilizing waste heat for other purposes, is becoming more prevalent. Since these cycle improvements are generally not applied to aircraft engines because of the weight penalty involved, aero-derivative engines are usually not able to use them.

The three possibilities for improving the gas turbine cycle – intercooling, regeneration and reheat - are shown together in Fig. 11.

Regeneration

The most common cycle improvement is regeneration where exhaust heat is used to increase the temperature of compressed air before combustion. This is accomplished by installing a heat exchanger in the exhaust to preheat the air between the compressor and the combustors.

This approach, which is becoming less common, allows the efficiency of the gas turbine to be improved by 15-20%. Disadvantages are the increased capital cost and the fact that there are increased pressure losses with the newer high-pressure ratio compressors. Instead, many installations now use the exhaust heat for combined cycle or cogeneration.

FIGURE 11

Intercooling Reheat And Regeneration

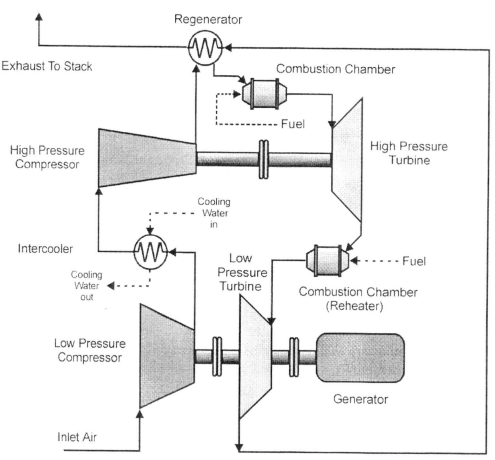

Intercooling

In some gas turbine arrangements, the compression of the inlet air is done in two stages with the air being cooled between the stages in a heat exchanger (intercooler). Since isothermal compression (compression without an increase in temperature) takes less work than adiabatic compression (compression where no heat is removed so that the air temperature increases), more of the turbine power will be available for the output load. Another advantage of intercooling is that the specific volume of the air is reduced, permitting a smaller physical size for the machine.

The beneficial effect of intercooling decreases as pressure ratio increases. A high-pressure ratio also means that losses through the intercooler become more significant. Using an intercooler is more beneficial if it is combined with regeneration as more of the exhaust heat will be recovered and this will improve the overall cycle efficiency.

The intercooler is a shell and tube heat exchanger similar in construction to the regenerator. Cooling water passes through the tubes while the air passes over the outside of the tubes. In some cases the air may pass through tubes surrounded by water.

Reheat

In addition to compressing the air in two stages and intercooling between these stages, the gas turbine plant may also be arranged to expand the hot gases in two stages, with the gases being reheated between the stages. The gases are expanded first in a high-pressure turbine and then reheated before entering a low-pressure turbine. The location of the reheater is shown in Fig. 11.

The effect of this reheating is to increase the energy content of the gases and thus improve the thermal efficiency of the cycle. As a result, less air must be compressed to do the same amount of work. The reheating is done by burning fuel in a second combustion chamber using the excess oxygen content of the gases from the high-pressure turbine for combustion.

Combined Cycle

Gas turbines can be integrated into a wide variety of combined cycle or cogeneration systems. Many of these are in use today, and their utilization is increasing. These systems usually extract the exhaust heat from the gas turbine by means of a heat exchanger, usually a type of boiler. Steam is produced, which can be used to drive a steam turbine, or to provide steam for process plant purposes or other heating applications. The steam turbine can be connected to the same generator as the gas turbine, another generator, a compressor or some other mechanical drive. An example is shown in Fig. 12.

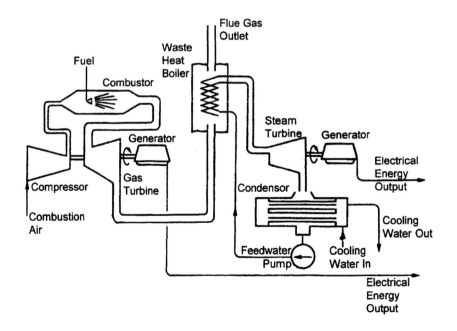

FIGURE 12

A Typical Combined Cycle

COMPRESSOR DESIGNS

A highly efficient and capable compressor is critical for the efficient operation of a gas turbine. Two types of compressors are used in gas turbines:

- Centrifugal or radial
- Axial

In small gas turbines, centrifugal compressors are often used, in combination with several axial stages. The majority of large gas turbines use a multi-stage axial compressor. Since the compressor absorbs up to ⅔ of the energy provided by the fuel, it must be structurally sound, as well as efficient.

CENTRIFUGAL (RADIAL) COMPRESSORS

These compressors take air in at the centre or "eye" of the rotor. Due to the high rotational speeds of the rotor, the air is accelerated by the blades and forced radially to the edge of the rotor at high velocity by centrifugal force. There, the air is received by the diffuser, which in turn, converts the high velocity to pressure energy. The components of a centrifugal compressor rotor are shown in Fig.13. A multistage centrifugal compressor design is shown in Fig. 14. Advantages of the radial or centrifugal compressor are simplicity, strength and short length.

FIGURE 13

Centrifugal Compressor

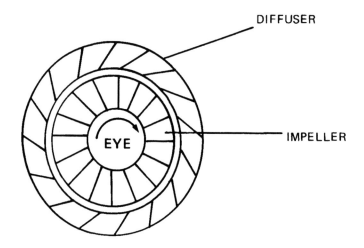

FIGURE 14

Multistage Centrifugal Compressor Rotor
(Courtesy of Elliott Company)

AXIAL COMPRESSORS

This type of compressor operates on a principle similar to a turbine, but acting in reverse. The moving blades act upon the air so as to increase its velocity and discharge it axially into the next row of fixed blades, rather as though each moving blade was a small section of a propeller. The fixed blades tend to slow the air down in its passage through them and so raise its pressure.

If the moving blades are properly shaped, they will cause the air to be compressed in its passage through them so that compression takes place in both fixed and moving blading. If the pressure rise in each is equal, the compressor is symmetrically staged and is similar to a reaction turbine (in reverse). An axial flow compressor rotor is shown in Fig. 15.

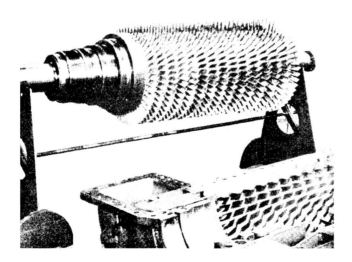

FIGURE 15

Multi-Stage Axial Compressor Rotor

COMBUSTORS

The combustion chamber, or combustor, in the open cycle gas turbine is used to heat the working air after its discharge from the compressor and before entry to the gas turbine. It must do this with a minimum loss of pressure and with the minimum of combustion impurities since these will be carried with the air into the turbine blading.

About 20 per cent of the air entering the combustor is mixed with the fuel in the flame tube as combustion air; the remainder - 80% - flows on the outside of the tube and services as cooling air.

The temperature of the burning gases in the tube will be 2500°F to 3000°F but the final mixture of the air and hot gas leaving the combustor is limited to the temperature that the turbine blading can withstand over its working life. This is about 1200 to 1300°F in present day practice so that the cooling air and hot gas must be thoroughly mixed before leaving the combustor.

Some of the gas turbine designs use a single, large volume combustor and others a series of smaller combustors disposed radially around the engine between the compressor and the turbine. Generally the large combustion chamber will be used when a regenerator is included in the plant or where heavy oil is to be the fuel used.

Fig. 16 shows a section of a combustion chamber of the single type as used by Brown Boveri. The air inlet is located low down and the air flows upwards between the inner and outer jackets. Approximately halfway up, some of the air is mixed with the combustion gases through adjustable mixing nozzle. The remaining air serves to cool the telescopically arranged cylindrical sections forming the inner tube, finally flowing through the annular spaces between sections. Almost 20% of the total inlet air reaches the top of the combustor and enters the swirler to act as combustion air for the fuel. An electrically heated ignition rod is positioned close to the swirler.

Fig. 17 illustrates a section through a combustor used by Associated Electrical Industries (Canada) Ltd. Six of these combustors are used on a machine of 6.5 MW (8,700 hp) output burning natural gas or distillate oil.

Each combustor is made up of an inner chamber, which is carried on radial pins to allow relative expansion, and an outer casing. Interconnecting pipes are provided between the six combustors to give uniform combustion conditions and to carry the flame from one to the other during the starting sequence, only two of the combustors carry igniter elements.

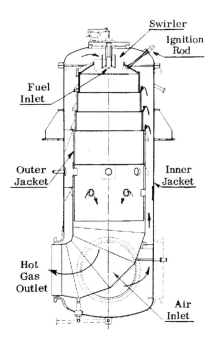

FIGURE 16

Gas Turbine Combustion Chamber
(Courtesy of Brown Boveri (Canada) Limited)

FIGURE 16

Gas Turbine Combustion Chamber Arrangement
(Courtesy of Associated Electrical Industries (Canada) Ltd.)

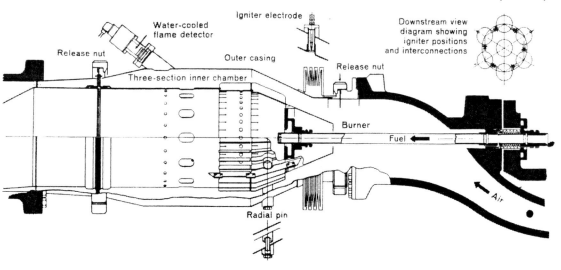

TYPES OF COMBUSTORS

There are three basic designs for combustors:

- Can-annular
- Annular
- Single-can

Can-Annular

In the can-annular design, combustion takes place in multiple combustors, also called combustion cans, which are placed around the centerline of the gas turbine. Some are straight through, as shown in Fig. 18. Usually these are older aero-derivative designs where minimum frontal area is important.

The advantage of a "Can" setup is that problems associated with aerodynamics and combustion, such as non-uniform outlet temperatures, are minimized. The disadvantages are that multiple igniters and fuel lines are required and also that the 'Can' setup is not the most efficient use of space in an annular volume.

FIGURE 18

Straight Through Can-Annular Combustor
(Courtesy of Rolls-Royce)

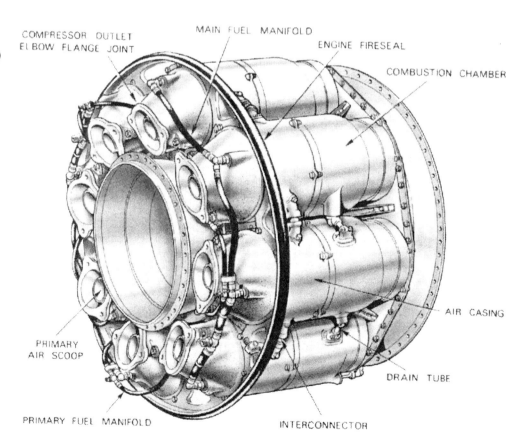

Annular

This type of combustion chamber, shown in Fig. 19, consists of a single concentric flame tube surrounding the spools. This is the most efficient use of the space available to the airflow. The main advantage of the annular combustion chamber is that for the same power output, there is up to 25 % reduction in the weight. As a single large combustion chamber, the combustion process is more evenly distributed in the tube.

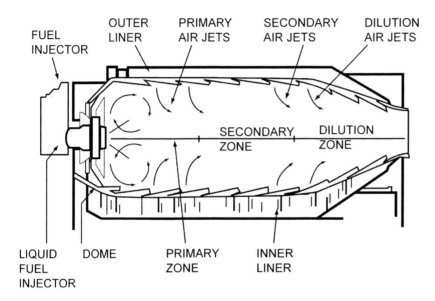

FIGURE 19

Annular Combustor Cross Section

Single Can

Chambers are arranged around the engine and the air is delivered into ducts in each chamber. Each chamber has an inner flame tube. All the tubes are interconnected which allows each tube to operate at the same pressure. The early axial flow compressor engines used this type of chamber. The burners are arranged in a circular fashion around the engine. Each chamber has a separate flame tube although they are all interconnected. Each tube operates at the same pressure, which provides identical operating conditions.

TURBINE DESIGN

The turbine extracts power from the hot gases supplied from the combustion section by decreasing pressure and temperature. It is used first to drive the compressor and then provides mechanical power for the generator, compressor or other load. As was discussed earlier, the turbine may be split into one, two or even three separate sections and shafts. Similar to compressors, turbines can be of the axial-flow or radial-inflow type although axial-flow turbines are much more common. Turbines operate at very high temperatures, high blade loading and large rotational stresses.

Axial-Flow Turbines

Because energy can be extracted much more efficiently, fewer stages are needed in the turbine than in the compressor. In the axial-flow turbine, a stage consists of a row of stationary blades, usually called nozzle guide vanes or nozzles, and a row of rotating blades, sometimes called buckets. The nozzles increase the velocity with a partial pressure drop and the moving blades extract power with a further drop in pressure and temperature. This design is usually of the impulse-reaction type.

In impulse turbines, the nozzles decrease in area to convert pressure into velocity and this kinetic energy is used to drive the turbine, which is of constant area. With reaction turbines, the nozzles are of constant area and serve only to redirect the flow at the right angle for the turbine blades, which have divergent passages to reduce pressure and increase velocity. All gas turbines utilize turbines of the impulse-reaction type, which is a combination of the two.

BLADE COOLING

Many gas turbines use air-cooled (and sometimes water-cooled) blades to reduce metal temperature and increase life. Air is supplied from the compressor section, circulated through the blade and then extracted through holes in the leading edge, trailing edge and surface of each blade. The incorporation of complicated cooling passages in turbine nozzles and blades is also a major manufacturing challenge that has resulted in many special techniques and methods.

TURBINE MATERIALS

The greatest challenges in gas turbine materials are in the turbine nozzles and blades, particularly the first stage. Conventional nozzles are cast with special nickel-based super alloys such as Inconel, Udimet, Waspalloy and Hastelloy. Gas turbine blading is made of heat resisting steel, forged and machined to shape. Steps are taken in some designs to cool the blading, using hollow blading with some coolant such as compressed air flowing through. Fig. 20 (a) and (b) show a turbine moving blade and a turbine fixed blading half diaphragm.

FIGURE 20

Gas Turbine Blades
(Courtesy of Associated Electrical Industries (Canada) Ltd.)

(a)   *(b)*

The stresses in the turbine rotors and blading are high because of the high gas temperatures. In order to withstand this, the rotors are made from heat resisting steel and, owing to the difficulty of making large forgings of this material, the rotors are generally made up of discs bolted or welded together. Fig. 21, (a) and (b), show a Westinghouse Gas turbine rotor of bolted construction.

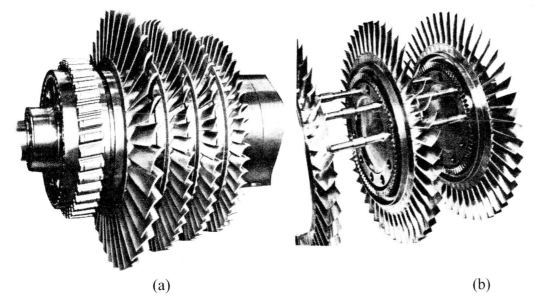

FIGURE 21

Gas Turbine Rotor Of Bolted Construction
(Courtesy of Canadian Westinghouse Company Limited)

(a)   (b)

Special casting techniques are now able to manufacture superior strength and temperature resistance. Ceramic components are becoming a reality and will allow a significant increase in firing temperatures.

At very high temperatures and stresses, materials suffer from a phenomenon called creep. This is a stretching of a material over time, which opens up voids and ultimately causes catastrophic rupture and failure of turbine blades. This usually requires replacement of turbine blades at a fixed interval, typically between 75,000 and 100,000 hours of operation.

CONTROL SYSTEMS

Control of a gas turbine is affected by varying the fuel flow to the nozzles according to operating requirements and conditions. Although the final control system configuration varies according to the application and type of fuel used, the block diagram, Fig. 22, shows some of the basic control units common to both liquid and gaseous fuel systems. The supply of pressurized fuel may come from a liquid fuel reservoir and engine-driven gear pumps incorporating a bypass system, or in the case of gaseous systems, directly from a gas supply line through a pressure regulator.

The gas turbine unit shown in the block diagram is a dual shaft machine with separate compressor drive (or gas producing) turbine and power turbine.

All-speed governing of the power turbine is used to control the speed and power output of the unit. A reset mechanism in the governor determines the position of the fuel metering valve and hence, controls the engine fuel flow.

Initially, the operator at the loading station sets the desired engine speed. This establishes a speed reference setting in the reset mechanism. If engine speed is above or below the setting, a proportional error signal is transmitted to the metering valve positioner. The valve is repositioned until the error is eliminated and the power turbine is at the desired output.

Various override trims, such as over temperature and overspeed protection for the gas producer, are applied on the governor reset mechanism through the loading station to produce an artificial error signal until the adverse condition is overcome.

To avoid compressor surge during acceleration, a separate signal, applied directly to the metering valve positioner, overrides the governor error signal. The acceleration fuel flow schedule is based on the rise in compressor outlet pressure.

An automatic emergency trip system closes the main fuel shutoff valve if:

- The lubricating oil pressure drops to an unsafe value
- The exhaust temperature exceeds the allowable limit
- Either of the rotor speeds becomes excessive

Manual shutdown is also affected through this circuit by means of a manual hydraulic valve.

FIGURE 22

Gas Turbine Control System

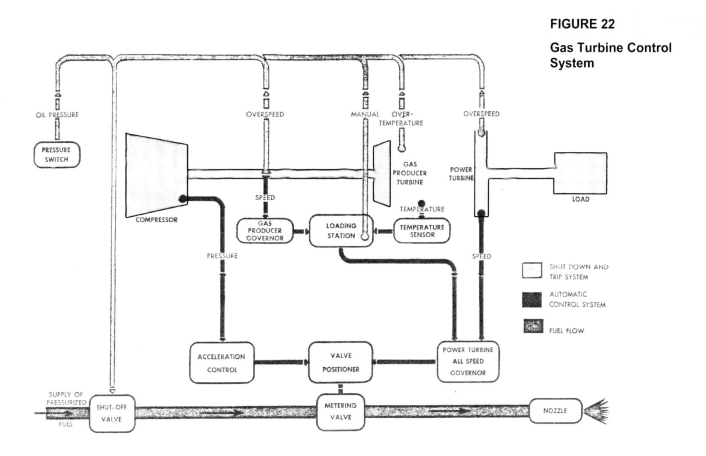

INSTRUMENTATION

The following instrumentation is normally provided for control and monitoring of a gas turbine:

- Rotor speed for each shaft, in r/min

- Air inlet temperature in °F, preferably after the intake filter but often ambient air temperature.

- Differential pressure across the intake filters

- Compressor discharge pressure measured at the exit of the compressor and before combustion, in psi

- Exhaust gas temperatures in °F, usually measured at multiple circumferential points and as an average after the first or second turbine stage or in between the engine turbine and power turbine

- Vibration, using accelerometers mounted on the engine case if anti-friction bearings are used (applies to most aero-derivatives)

- Vibration using eddy-current displacement probes if journal or tilt-pad bearings are used (applies to most heavy-duty gas turbines)

- Bearing temperatures in °F if journal or tilt-pad bearings are used (applies to most heavy-duty gas turbines)

- Fuel gas flow, pressure and temperature

- Oil system pressures and temperatures

- Generator output, in kW, hp or compressor shaft power

Operator Interface

With every control system, there is an operator interface (sometimes called an MMI – Man Machine Interface or HMI – Human Machine Interface). It allows an operator to:

- Startup or shutdown the gas turbine
- Control the turbines speed
- Modify the control system logic, with special access only
- Monitor measured parameters

Startup and Shutdown Sequencing

The startup and shutdown of a gas turbine may occur automatically if predetermined conditions occur. For example, a backup power generation unit may start if there is an increase in demand and a compressor may start if the pressure drops in a process. Often, operators monitoring the overall process will initiate a manual start. Once the start or shutdown is initiated, the sequencing is almost always automatic.

Protection

A number of protective devices will first alarm and then shutdown the engine if certain levels are exceeded. They normally protect against:

- Power turbine overspeed
- Exhaust gas temperatures higher than the maximum limit
- Excessive vibration
- Excessive oil and bearing temperatures
- Fuel gas pressure too low or too high
- Excessive air intake filter differential pressure

OPERATING PARAMETERS

The operation of a gas turbine is defined by a number of operating parameters that consist mainly of flows, pressures and temperatures along the gas path of the engine. It is possible to produce a map of these parameters, such as the one shown in Fig. 23, which shows the interrelationship between these parameters over a range of operating conditions up to some predetermined maximum limit. Producers of gas turbines provide electrical production performance data in terms of the heat rate input. Heat rate is the amount of joules (Btu's) required to produce one kWh of electrical energy (MJ/kWh).

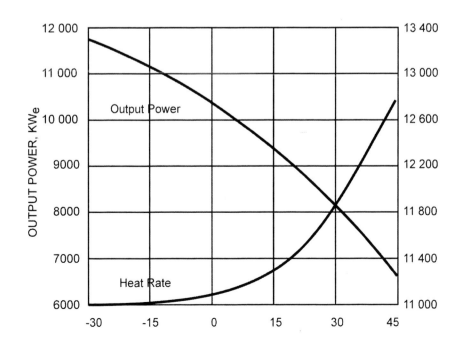

FIGURE 23

Performance Graph For a Gas Turbine

Effect of Inlet Air Temperature

The temperature of the air entering the gas turbine has a great impact on its operation and performance. As the air temperature decreases, its density increases and the mass airflow through the engine increases, accordingly. The power that is produced by the gas turbine is proportional to the mass flow. Therefore, a gas turbine will produce more power at lower ambient temperatures. This is the basis for using heat exchangers that increase power by cooling the inlet air.

From Fig. 23, it can be seen that the rated power at standard conditions of 60°F is 9500 kW (12.5 million Btu). At 115°F, the power output drops to approximately 6600 kW (8,800 Btu). At an ambient air temperature of -20°F, the power output is almost 12 000 kW (16 million Btu).

Effect of Compressor Discharge Pressure and Turbine Inlet Temperature

The two major factors in determining efficiency and power are compression ratio across the compressor and turbine inlet temperature:

- The greater the compressor ratio, the higher is the cycle efficiency and the greater the power output.

- An increase in the turbine inlet temperature has the same effect because more work is done by the same amount of air.

Although factors, such as compressor and turbine efficiency and pressure losses, are important, the largest efforts in gas turbine design have been to increase the compression ratio and to improve combustion and turbine materials so that the turbine inlet temperature can be increased. With these improvements, simple cycle efficiency has now reached 40%. With combined cycle applications, the total efficiency of the gas turbine plant can exceed 60%.

Maximum Power

The maximum power that can be achieved is also a function of the life expected of the hot gas path components. Vendors usually specify a maximum power that will permit the engine to achieve a reasonable life. They also specify a maximum peak power limit that can be applied if a user is willing to incur higher maintenance costs. This tradeoff is sometimes used for peak power generation where gas turbines operate for only short periods of time to satisfy peak load conditions. For base load operation, this is not desirable because of the increased maintenance costs and the risk of failure.

UNIT 3

Gas Turbine Design and Auxiliaries

Learning Objectives

Here is what you will be able to do when you complete each objective:

1. Explain applications and selection criteria for the different types of gas turbine engines.

2. Describe the principles and design of open and closed cycle gas turbine systems.

3. Describe the principles and design of combined cycle and cogeneration systems using gas turbines.

4. Describe the principles and design of gas turbine regeneration, intercooling, and reheating.

5. Describe the principles and design of gas turbine shaft arrangements.

6. Describe the design and components of gas turbine compressors, combustors (combustion chambers) and turbines.

7. Describe the design and operation of gas turbine air intake and exhaust systems.

8. Describe the design and operation of a gas turbine lubricating oil system.

9. Describe the design and operation of a gas turbine fuel system.

10. Describe the design and operation of a gas turbine steam or water injection system and a dry low NOx system.

INTRODUCTION

Gas turbine engines are becoming a major source of power for many industrial applications. There are a wide range of designs and configurations available to meet the varied needs of industry. The simple cycle gas turbine provides a very efficient and capable solution which can be further improved when combined with exhaust heat recovery and other methods.

APPLICATIONS

Industrial gas turbines are used for a very wide range of applications, including:
- Base load power generation (ranging from small 30kW microturbines to large (250MW – 650MW) turbines used in combined cycle power plants)
- Backup power generation and peak loading
- Natural gas compression (from the wellhead to gas transmission and distribution)
- Combined cycle applications (produce power from the prime load and from steam recovered from the exhaust gas by means of a heat exchanger)
- Cogeneration (of power and heat for use in steam, heating, and other applications)
- Various process plant applications (such as a mechanical drive, usually used for compression)
- Offshore power generation and compression
- Ship propulsion
- Vehicle propulsion (particularly heavy-duty trucks)
- Fast trains

TYPES OF GAS TURBINES

There are two basic types of gas turbines used in industrial applications:
- Aero-derivative gas turbines (derived from aircraft engines)
- Heavy-duty gas turbines (designed for industrial applications)

Aero-Derivative Gas Turbines

Aero-derivative gas turbines are aircraft engines adapted for industrial use, either by:

- Adding a power turbine to drive the load
- Converting a turboprop engine which already has a power turbine

An example of the first type, a Rolls Royce RB211-24C, is shown in Fig. 1. It was introduced in 1974 and is still in production, although many changes have been made. Like most aero-derivatives, the design is simple, compact, and lightweight.

FIGURE 1

Rolls Royce RB211 Gas Turbine (26.1 MW)
(Courtesy of Tom Van Hardeveld)

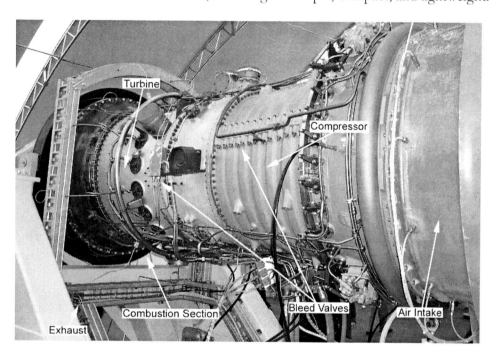

In general, aero-derivative gas turbines are:
- Suitable for locations such as offshore platforms, ships, trains, and vehicles where **high power to weight ratio** is critical
- Easily maintained and can be removed and replaced quite quickly which maximizes on-line time and availability
- Fast startup and loading capability, which is critical for backup power generation and certain process applications
- Less durable than heavy-duty industrial type gas turbines and, under the same conditions, will usually have a shorter life span
- High efficiency and power output
- Able to use a variety of gaseous and liquid fuels and can be designed to operate on mixed fuels if required

Heavy Duty Gas Turbines

Heavy duty gas turbines have many of the same basic design features as steam turbines, compressors and axial and radial air and gas compressors. Since the overall equipment size and weight is not as much of an issue with industrial type gas turbines, the layout is more flexible and they will be designed using heavier and more rugged materials than aero-derivatives. An example of an industrial type gas turbine is the General Electric 6FA (107 MW) shown in Fig. 2.

FIGURE 2

GE Frame 6FA Heavy-Duty Gas Turbine
(Courtesy of GE Power Systems)

Heavy-duty or industrial type gas turbines have the following general characteristics:

- Physically larger, more rugged and heavier than aero-derivatives
- More durable than aero-derivatives which allows long intervals between overhauls and gives a longer life cycle with increased on-line time
- Very efficient with quick start-up and loading capabilities
- Able to use a wide variety of gas and liquid fuels
- Design and layout of compressor, combustors, turbine and load is more flexible than aero-derivatives
- Potential for inter-cooling, regeneration, reheat and other custom options that increase cycle efficiency and allow for combined cycle and cogeneration operation

However, heavy-duty designs do vary, and some, such as those manufactured by Solar Turbines (4.57MW), are a hybrid of aero-derivative and heavy-duty gas turbines, as shown in Fig. 3.

FIGURE 3

Solar Centaur 50 Gas Turbine
(Reprinted Courtesy of Solar Turbines Incorporated)

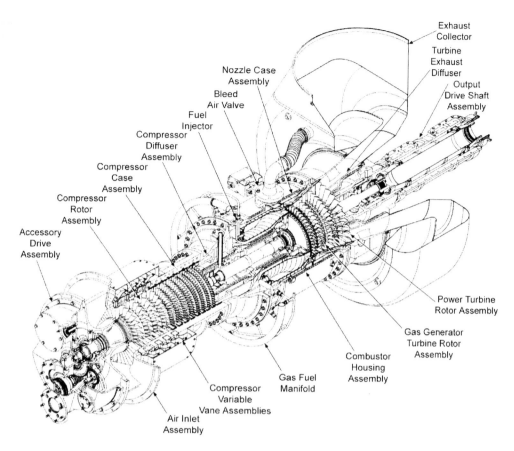

SELECTION

The successful application of any engine depends on satisfying requirements related to desired performance, cost-effective operation, and expected engine life. This requires a thorough understanding of the designs available and engine rating systems, as well as knowledge of tradeoffs that might need to be made. A trade off may be, for example, a more robust turbine (higher cost) but with a longer engine life.

The selection of a gas turbine engine for a specific application depends on factors such as:

- Performance ratings
- Weight and size restrictions
- Type of fuel available
- Maintenance support resources
- Life cycle costs

Performance Ratings

The performance rating and required range of power output are important factors to consider when choosing a specific gas turbine. Gas turbines operate most efficiently when running full loaded. Although they can operate down to 50% of full load rating, the lower operating ranges will cause the turbine output efficiency to drop substantially, down into the 30% to 40% range.

This makes it important to choose a gas turbine that operates at, or near, its maximum power capabilities. Smaller gas turbines are less efficient, although waste heat recovery or combined cycle applications can be very efficient. For short-term peak power applications, a gas turbine can sometimes be run at higher than rated power output, but this practice will reduce the life cycle of the turbine and cause an increase in maintenance and repair costs.

Weight and Size Restrictions

Weight and size restrictions usually favour gas turbines over other types of engines, such as reciprocating internal combustion engines, especially for higher power applications. Aero-derivative engines normally provide the lowest-weight solution.

Type of Fuel Available

The type of fuel available needs to be considered. The cleanest and most accessible fuel should be used. Pipeline quality natural gas is desirable because it delivers the most efficient, cost-effective, and environmentally acceptable solution. Lower quality gaseous fuels such as landfill or sewage gas require special handling and delivery systems and, due to their lower kJ values, will result in lower power output and turbine efficiencies. Liquid fuel, such as kerosene, provides reliable operation but may be unsuitable where emissions are an issue, or where fuel sources are not easily accessible. Lower grade liquid fuels may be cost-effective, but require fuel treatment and could result in higher maintenance costs.

Maintenance Support Resources

Maintenance has to be taken into consideration before a final selection is made. This includes the availability of skilled personnel, spare parts, and other support requirements.

Life Cycle Costs

Life cycle costs include not only the initial capital investment, but also fuel, operating, and maintenance costs. Simple cycle gas turbines are now efficient enough to compete with other types of engines on a cost basis. The use of gas turbines in combined cycle applications provides an efficient solution over the life cycle of the engine.

When selecting a gas turbine engine, it is important to consult with manufacturers on recommendations for proper application, engine rating, and equipment configuration.

THE GAS TURBINE CYCLE

A knowledge of thermodynamic principles helps to understand the operation of gas turbines. Gas turbines can use one of two basic cycles — the open cycle or the closed cycle. This objective presents the simple versions of the open and closed cycle. A detailed description of the simple gas turbine cycle will be given here to allow the reader to grasp the key concepts and operating principles involved. Combined and cogeneration cycles will be covered further in the module.

The gas turbine thermodynamic cycle, called the Brayton cycle, is shown in Fig. 4. It consists of four steps:
1. The air is compressed, which increases the pressure and temperature and decreases the volume (from stage 1 to stage 2).
2. Heat is added, which results in a major increase in temperature and a small increase in volume, but almost no change in pressure (from stage 2 to stage 3).
3. Then, the air is expanded through the turbine and produces mechanical work. Pressure decreases to near atmospheric level. The temperature also decreases, although the air is still quite hot when it exits (from stage 3 to stage 4).
4. The air is cooled to ambient conditions and returns to its original volume and density (from stage 4 to stage 1).

Note: a significant part of the work of the turbine ($W_{33'}$) is used to run the compressor. The remaining energy extracted ($W_{3'4}$) is available to drive the load.

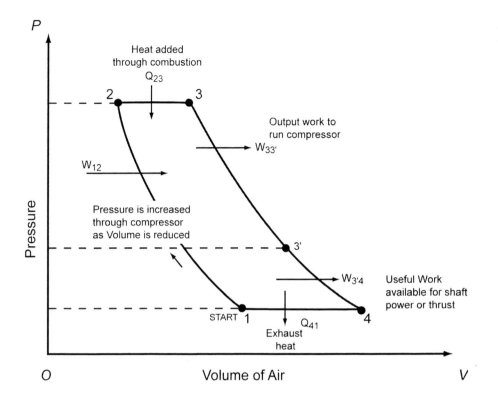

FIGURE 4

The Brayton Cycle

Open Cycle

Gas turbines almost always use the open cycle. Air is drawn from the atmosphere into the turbine, and then exhausted back to the atmosphere at the end of the cycle. Fuel is added to the air in the combustor section and combustion occurs inside the gas turbine.

An open cycle model of the Brayton cycle is shown in Fig. 5 and consists of four steps:

1. The air is compressed in a compressor (stage 1 to stage 2)
2. Fuel is added and combusted in a combustor (from stage 2 to stage 3).
3. The air expands, first through a turbine that runs the compressor, and then through a separate turbine that drives the load (from stage 3 to stage 4).
4. The air is exhausted to the atmosphere where it cools to ambient conditions and returns to its original volume and density (stage 4).

FIGURE 5

The Open Cycle Gas Turbine

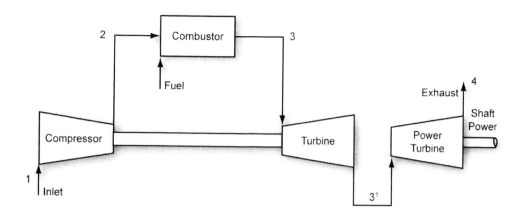

Closed Cycle

The closed cycle is similar to the open cycle except that the working fluid (air) remains in the cycle instead of being exhausted to the atmosphere. This offers a number of thermodynamic advantages but at the expense of a more complicated configuration. This means that:

- The fluid has to be heated by a heat exchanger that will have the combustion process separate from the cycle fluid
- The fluid needs to be cooled after expanding through the turbine

Closed cycle systems are used less often than open cycle systems. Open cycle gas turbines are more efficient and combined cycle applications offer a better solution than closed cycle systems.

The simple closed cycle (Fig. 6) consists of the following steps:

1. The fluid is compressed in a compressor.
2. The fluid is heated in a heat exchanger. Since it passes through tubes which are surrounded by combustion gases, the fluid and the burning fuel do not come in direct contact with each other.
3. The fluid expands, first through a turbine that runs the compressor, and then through a separate turbine that drives the load.
4. The fluid is cooled in a heat exchanger before being compressed again.

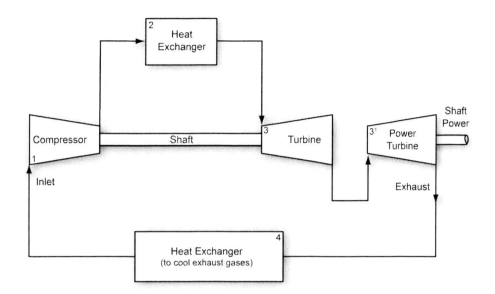

FIGURE 6

The Closed Cycle Gas Turbine

Advantages of the closed cycle are:

- The working fluid pressure can be much higher than open cycle system pressure. Higher pressure means that the working fluid has a higher density. Therefore, a greater mass of the fluid expands through the turbine producing more power.

- Combustion products do not mix with the working fluid. Thus, there is no fouling of turbine blades or heat exchanger surfaces, and therefore a wider variety of fuels can be used.

- A working fluid with a greater heat transfer coefficient than air can be used, such as helium which has approximately twice the heat transfer coefficient of air. This reduces the amount of heating surface required in the heat exchangers.

Disadvantages of the closed cycle are:

- The initial cost is higher than that of an open cycle system because of the heat exchangers (air cooler and air heater).

- More space is required because the unit is larger due to the extra components.

- A steady supply of cooling water is required.

COMBINED CYCLE AND COGENERATION SYSTEMS

The exhaust gases from gas turbines contain a large amount of heat energy that is available for use to generate steam or to heat process fluids throughout the facility. Utilizing this waste energy can greatly increase the overall efficiency of the system and make the selection of a gas turbine much more advantageous to the engineer.

Exhaust temperatures can range from 400°C to 600°C. This heat can be partially recovered by a waste heat recovery system. Thermal efficiency can be increased from a simple cycle efficiency of 30%-40% to a total plant efficiency of 60%-70%. To avoid corrosion, the final temperature should not be reduced below the dew point.

A combined cycle uses the waste heat energy in the exhaust gases to provide additional steam generating capability for the facility. The combined cycle approach is ideal for use in large base load power generation applications that can exceed 1000 MW of total power. If the waste heat produces steam or hot water that is used for heating, cooling, or general steam applications, it is called a cogeneration or combined heat and power (CHP) system.

Combined Cycle Design

In a combined cycle design, the exhaust gases are routed to a Heat Recovery Steam Generator (HRSG) that supplies steam to a steam turbine. The steam turbine can be used to drive a separate generator (Fig. 7) or, in some cases, it can be attached directly to the same generator as the gas turbine (Fig. 8).

FIGURE 7

Separate Generators with Common Steam Turbine

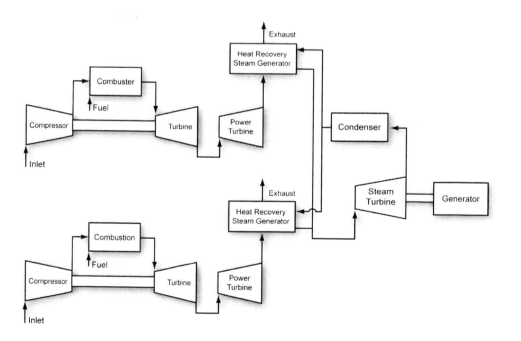

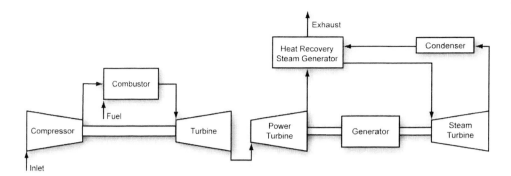

FIGURE 8

Single Generator with Steam Turbine on Common Shaft

The HRSG may be unfired (no extra heat is added), or it may be fired. In the fired type, an additional burner, or multiples of burners, will be installed in the ducting just upstream of the HRSG to increase the temperature of the exhaust gases.

The advantages of the fired system are that it:

- Compensates for changes in gas turbine output to give constant steam production
- Can be used when the turbine is at low loads or not on at all to generate steam for the facility

Early combined cycle installations used a single-pressure HRSG. Now HRSGs often use a double-pressure or triple-pressure configuration, such as the one shown in Fig. 9. This extracts the greatest amount of heat and results in a more efficient operation. The choice of HRSG depends on the temperature of the exhaust. A triple-pressure HRSG is the best option for gas turbines with a high firing temperature (above 550°C).

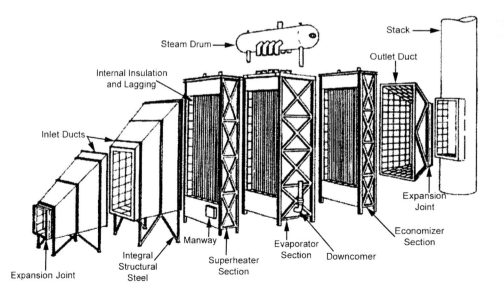

FIGURE 9

Triple-pressure HRSG
(Courtesy of GE Power Systems)

Cogeneration Design

Cogeneration designs are used in distributed power applications. An example is shown in Fig. 10. The two gas turbines (GT) each produce 1 550kW of electrical power. Their exhaust is fed to a common HRSG, which has supplementary firing, so that the amount of steam can be varied. Each engine has a diverter valve in case steam is not required.

FIGURE 10

Cogeneration Exhaust and Steam System

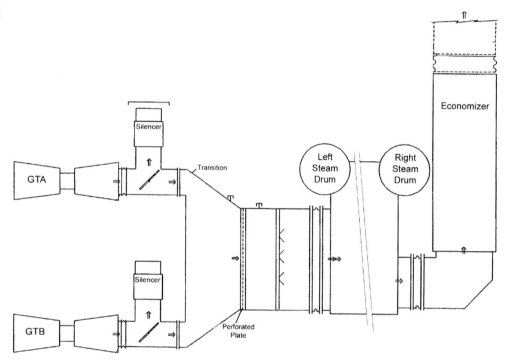

CYCLE IMPROVEMENTS

Three approaches — **regeneration, intercooling, reheat** — can be used to improve the efficiency of the basic gas turbine cycle. For various compatibility reasons, these are normally used independently and, at the moment, no gas turbine exists that uses all three methods. Aero-derivative engines are designed to be as light as possible to allow them to function efficiently as airplane engines. Therefore, they will not have the extra equipment included with them to allow for cycle improvements like industrial type turbines do. As simple cycle gas turbines are becoming more efficient, these cycle improvements are becoming less necessary. Furthermore, combined cycle designs, which use waste heat for other purposes, are becoming more prevalent.

Regeneration

The most common cycle improvement was the regenerative cycle, or regeneration. A heat exchanger installed in the exhaust preheats the air between the compressor and the combustors, as shown in Fig. 11. Thus, exhaust heat is used to increase the temperature of the compressed air prior to combustion. This approach was quite common since it improved the efficiency of the gas turbine by 15% to 20%.

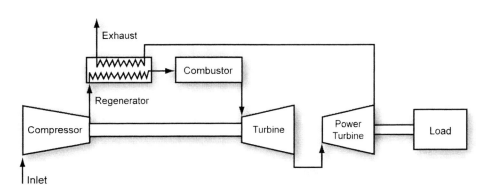

FIGURE 11

Regeneration

Disadvantages of regeneration include increased capital costs and pressure losses due to the high pressure ratio compressors. Instead of regeneration, many installations use the exhaust heat for combined cycle or cogeneration applications.

Intercooling

In some gas turbines, inlet air is compressed in two stages using a dual shaft arrangement. The air is cooled between the stages in a heat exchanger, or intercooler (Fig. 12). Since isothermal compression (compression without an increase in air temperature) takes less work than adiabatic compression (compression without removing heat which increases the air temperature), more turbine power is available for the output load. Another advantage of intercooling is that the total mass of air that needs to be circulated through the cycle per kW of energy produced is reduced.

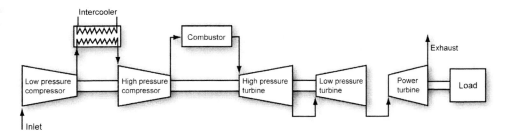

However, the beneficial effects of intercooling decrease as the pressure ratio increases. A high pressure ratio means that losses through the intercooler become significant. Using an intercooler makes more sense when combined with regeneration because more exhaust heat can be recovered. This improves the overall cycle efficiency.

Intercoolers are shell and tube heat exchangers similar in construction to regenerators. Cooling water passes through the tubes while air passes on the shell side. In some cases, air passes through tubes surrounded by water. The General Electric LM6000 has an innovative intercooling option, shown in Fig. 13, which introduces an atomized water spray between the low pressure and high pressure compressors. This provides a 9% power boost at 15°C and 20% at 32°C, without requiring a separate heat exchanger. A second water spray is injected into the air intake to reduce the temperature, and thus increase the power output.

FIGURE 13

Intercooling Using Water Spray
(Courtesy of GE Power Systems)

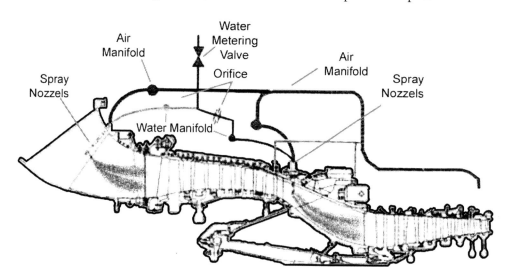

Reheat

Reheat cycles are fairly rare, but some gas turbines still use them. The hot gas is expanded in two stages and reheated between stages. After leaving the first set of combustion chambers, the gas is expanded through a high pressure turbine. Then, it passes through a second set of combustion chambers before entering a low pressure turbine where it is expanded a second time (see Fig. 14). The second set of combustion chambers uses the excess oxygen content of the gas exiting the high pressure turbine for combustion.

Reheating increases the energy content of the gas and improves the thermal efficiency of the cycle. As a result, less air has to be compressed in order to do the same amount of work.

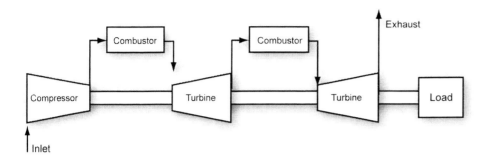

FIGURE 14

Reheat

SHAFT ARRANGEMENTS

Gas turbines are designed with a number of different shaft arrangements including:

- Single shaft
- Dual shaft
- Multi-shaft arrangements

Single Shaft

In the single shaft arrangement, the compressor, turbine, and load are connected and rotate at the same speed (see Fig. 15). This arrangement is used for power generation where a constant speed is required, but is rarely used for other applications because the power output is not flexible. Mechanically, it is simpler than a two-shaft arrangement, but requires a larger starting motor because it must also rotate the generator (load) up to ignition speed. The hot end drive arrangement, Fig. 15(a), is more common than the cold end drive that is shown in Fig. 15(b).

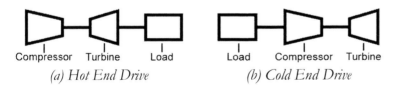

(a) Hot End Drive   *(b) Cold End Drive*

FIGURE 15 (a) (b)

Shaft Layouts – Single Shaft

The General Electric 6001, shown in Fig. 16, is an example of a hot end drive (the load is connected to the turbine).

FIGURE 16

General Electric 6001 – Single Shaft Gas Turbine with Hot End Drive
(Courtesy of GE Power Systems)

The Alstom Typhoon, shown in Fig. 17, is an example of a cold end drive arrangement.

FIGURE 17

Alstom Typhoon – Single Shaft Gas Turbine with Cold End Drive
(Courtesy of Alstom)

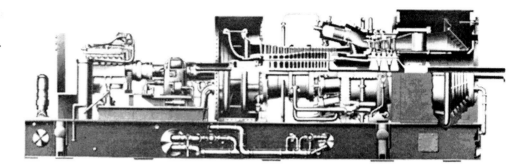

Typhoon (ISO) 4.35 MW(e)	PRESSURE	PSIA	14.7	188.4	183.6	14.7
		kPa	101.3	1299	1266	101.3
	TEMPERATURE	°C	15	371	1070	546
		°F	59	698	1958	1015
Typhoon (ISO) 4.70 MW(e)	PRESSURE	PSIA	14.7	200.4	195.3	14.7
		kPa	101.3	1382	1347	101.3
	TEMPERATURE	°C	15	387	1070	540
		°F	59	728	1958	1004
Typhoon (ISO) 5.05 MW(e)	PRESSURE	PSIA	14.7	209.5	204.2	14.7
		kPa	101.3	1445	1408	101.3
	TEMPERATURE	°C	15	400	1110	550
		°F	59	751	2030	1022
Typhoon (ISO) 5.25 MW(e)	PRESSURE	PSIA	14.7	217.5	214	14.7
		kPa	101.3	1500	1476	101.3
	TEMPERATURE	°C	15	405	1110	552
		°F	59	761	2030	1026

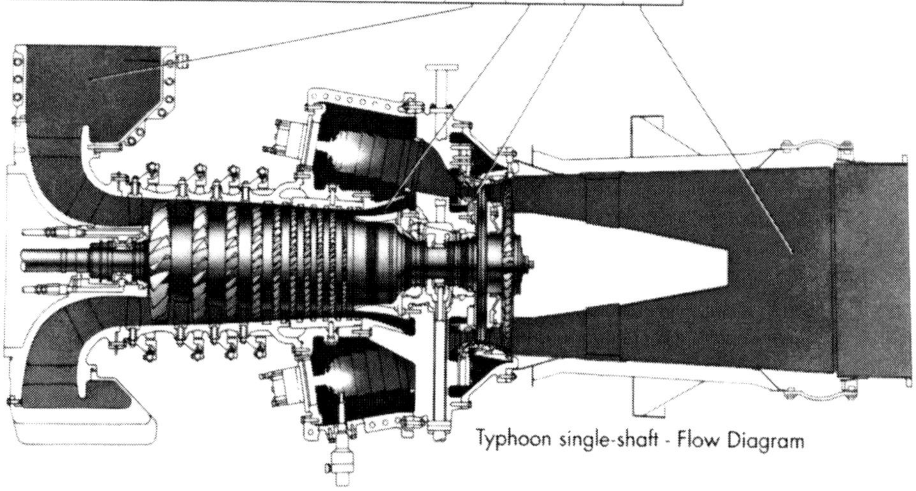

Typhoon single-shaft - Flow Diagram

Dual Shaft

The dual shaft (twin-shaft) arrangement, shown in Fig. 18, is the most common design. The compressor and turbine are connected by a shaft, but the power turbine (also called the free turbine) is coupled on a second shaft with the load. This layout provides more operational flexibility with respect to speed and load, especially for compressors.

Many gas turbines use dual shaft designs with the load coupled to the gas turbine (hot end) such those shown in Fig. 18 (a) and Fig. 19.

A cold end drive (the load is coupled to the compressor) positions the power turbine and load shaft inside the compressor turbine shaft as shown in Fig. 18 (b). This arrangement is much less common, although it does exist.

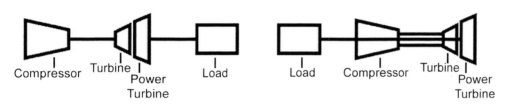

(a) Hot End Drive   *(b) Cold End Drive*

FIGURE 18 (a) (b)

Shaft Layouts – Dual Shaft

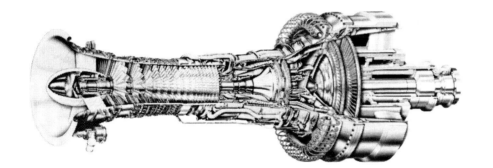

FIGURE 19

General Electric LM2500 – Dual Shaft Gas Turbine with Hot End Drive
(Courtesy of GE Power Systems)

Multi-Shaft

Fig. 20 (a) shows a fairly common aero-derivative design that uses a two-shaft arrangement for the engine, and a third shaft for the power turbine. The low-pressure compressor and turbine are connected by a shaft fitted inside the hollow shaft connecting the high-pressure compressor and turbine. Mechanically, this design is more complicated (especially for the bearings), but offers greater efficiency and operational flexibility. An even more complicated layout positions the load at the cold end, which requires three shafts on the same centerline, as shown in Fig. 20 (b).

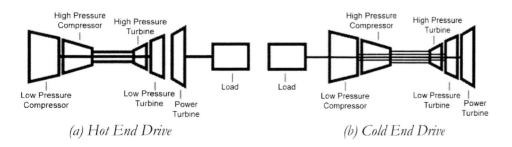

(a) Hot End Drive   *(b) Cold End Drive*

FIGURE 20 (a) (b)

Shaft Layouts – Triple Shaft

An example of this design, the Rolls Royce RB211 shown in Fig. 21; is widely used for both power generation and mechanical drive applications, such as compressors.

FIGURE 21

**Rolls Royce RB211 –
Triple Shaft Gas
Turbine with Hot End
Drive**
(Courtesy of Rolls Royce)

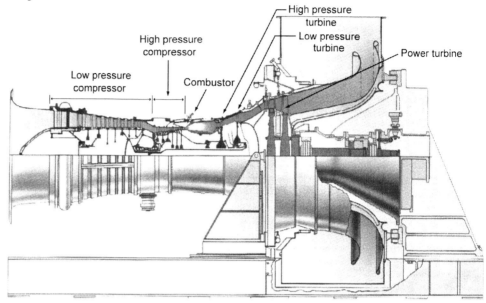

The General Electric LM6000, shown in Fig. 22, uses a unique design. It is similar to the triple shaft arrangement shown above, but the load is directly connected to either the low-pressure compressor, or the low-pressure turbine.

FIGURE 22

**Shaft Layouts – Direct
Dual Shaft**

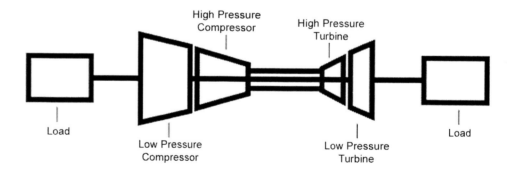

This engine, with optional cold end or hot end drive, is used exclusively for power generation and is shown in Fig. 23.

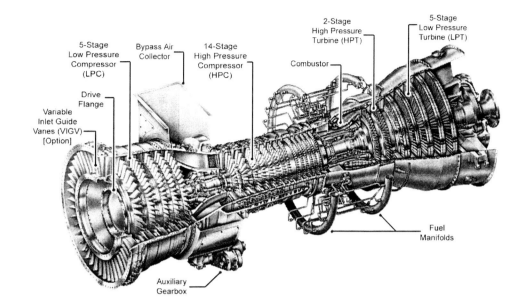

5-Stage
Low Pressure
Compressor
(LPC)

Bypass Air
Collector

14-Stage
High Pressure
Compressor
(HPC)

2-Stage
High Pressure
Turbine (HPT)

5-Stage
Low Pressure
Turbine (LPT)

Combustor

Drive
Flange

Variable
Inlet Guide
Vanes (VIGV)
[Option]

Fuel
Manifolds

Auxiliary
Gearbox

FIGURE 23

**General Electric
LM6000 –Dual Shaft
Gas Turbine**
*(Courtesy of GE Power
Systems)*

COMPRESSOR DESIGN

Highly efficient and effective compressors are essential for efficient gas turbine operation. Two types of compressors are used: axial and centrifugal (or radial). Small gas turbines often use centrifugal compressors, sometimes in combination with several axial stages. Large gas turbines almost always use multi-stage axial compressors.

To increase compressor efficiency, especially at lower speeds, multi-shaft arrangements may be used so that the initial stages can operate at lower speeds than the later stages.

Compressor designs often use a combination of inlet guide vanes (IGV's), variable stator vanes (VSV's), and bleed valves to counteract the effects of surge, which happens at lower speeds. This is described later in this module.

Axial Compressors

Axial compressors are similar to propellers; the air moves parallel to the axis of rotation. Since the mass flow through the compressor is constant, the area must decrease from the inlet to the outlet of the compressor. This means that the blades are largest in the first stage, and then get progressively smaller.

An axial compressor has multiple stages. An initial row of stationary blades, called the inlet guide vanes, is used to direct the air (at the correct angle) into the first stage of rotor blades. In each stage, a row of moving blades (rotors) is followed by a row of stationary blades (stators). Each stage has a small compression ratio, usually between 1.1:1 and 1.4:1. A compression ratio of between 10:1 and 40:1 can be achieved by all stages in combination.

Due to the diverging shape of the rotating and stationary blades in an axial compressor, the pressure of the fluid is increased across both sections of blades. Each row of rotor blades increases the velocity and the pressure of the air. The subsequent row of stator blades act as a diffuser which further increases pressure and decreases velocity.

The axial compressor rotor blade, shown in Fig. 24, shows the slender shape compressor blades need to maximize efficiency. Notice the twist in the blade which produces the optimum aerodynamic angle when the air enters into each compressor stage. The angle increases with the radius because velocity is higher at the tip of the blade than at the root.

FIGURE 24

Rolls Royce RB211 Gas Turbine
(Courtesy of Tom Van Hardeveld)

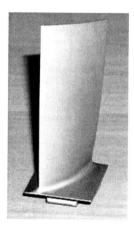

A cross-section of the axial compressor from a General Electric LM2500 is shown in Fig. 25. Note that the cooling flow from the 9th stage of the compressor is fed back through the intake strut to cool and pressurize the inside of the shaft, and the front, centre, and rear bearings. A bleed valve, coming off the 13th stage, cools the high pressure turbine nozzles.

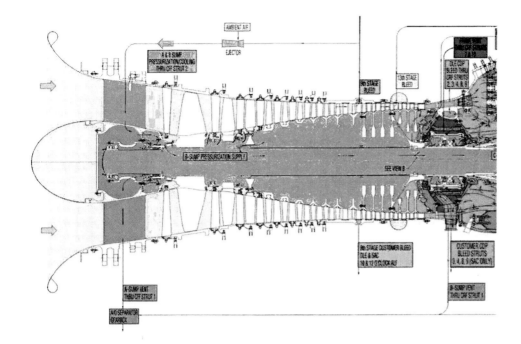

FIGURE 25

General Electric LM2500 Gas Turbine *(Courtesy of GE Power Systems)*

Centrifugal Compressors

Centrifugal compressors were initially widely used in gas turbines because they were more efficient and rugged than axial compressors. They are similar in basic design to the centrifugal compressors used throughout the various processes to compress fluids like air and natural gas vapours. Centrifugal compressors can achieve a higher per stage compression ratio, up to 9:1, than axial compressors.

A centrifugal compressor uses an impeller to accelerate the air and partially increase the pressure. A diffuser, which follows the impeller, further increases the pressure. Multiple impellers may be used (sometimes designed back-to-back), or they may be combined with several axial stages.

The Kawasaki M1A-13A gas turbine, shown in Fig. 26, has two centrifugal compressors mounted on a single shaft with the turbine and a gearbox connected to a generator.

FIGURE 26

Kawasaki M1A-13A Gas Turbine

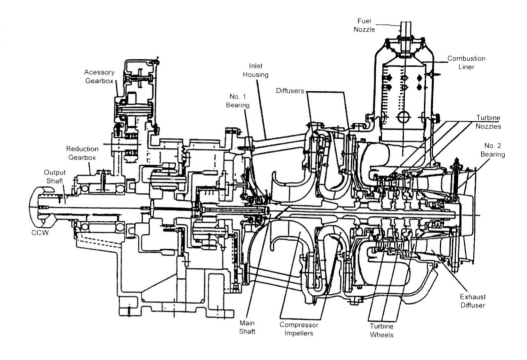

Compressor Surge

At lower speeds, since the blades are not at the optimum angle, air flow separation can occur. This is similar to an aircraft wing stalling or losing lift. When starting a gas turbine, the pressure rise is very low, and the compressor is trying to push the air into a much smaller area, designed for a larger compression ratio, at the back of the compressor. This can cause the air to choke. The result is called surge or rotating stall. It is a very complicated aerodynamic phenomenon that is not fully understood.

However, the methods required to counteract it are well developed. Two basic options used for countering surge are **bleed valves** and **variable compressor geometry**, but surge can still occur if the blades become dirty or fouled.

Bleed Valves

A bleed valve reduces the likelihood of surge by dumping air to increase air flow through the compressor during startup. When the blades reach a predetermined speed, the valve closes. The Rolls Royce RB211 Gas Turbine, shown in Fig. 1, has one bleed valve at the exit of the first compressor rotor, and one at exit of the second compressor rotor, which activate at different speeds.

The Solar Centaur 50 Gas Turbine, shown in Fig.3, has one bleed valve at the end of the compressor which feeds into the exhaust. Sometimes, multiple bleed valves are used.

Variable Compressor Geometry

Variable compressor geometry is used on many gas turbines to improve efficiency at part load and reduce the likelihood of surge during startup. One or more stages of stator vanes, either inlet guide vanes (IGVs) or variable stator vanes (VSVs), are rotated to optimize the airflow through the compressor according to the operating conditions —speed and temperature.

Most gas turbines have variable IGVs, such as the ones shown in Fig. 27. They are held in place by a ring around the outside of the compressor stage and actuated by hydraulics (see Fig. 28). During startup, the blades rotate to a closed position and restrict the flow of air. At a specified speed, they begin to open until they reach a predetermined angle.

FIGURE 27

Rolls Royce RB211 Gas Turbine Inlet Guide Vanes
(Courtesy of Tom Van Hardeveld)

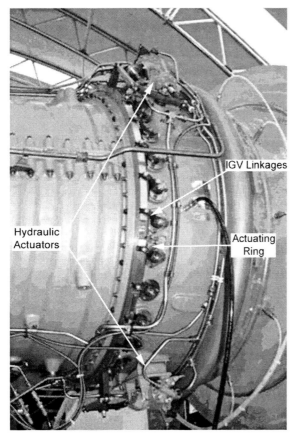

FIGURE 28

Rolls Royce RB211 Gas Turbine Inlet Guide Vane Linkage
(Courtesy of Tom Van Hardeveld)

Some engines use multiple stages of VSVs downstream of the IGV. The Solar Centaur 50 Gas Turbine, in Fig. 3, has three additional VSVs in addition to the IGV. They actuate from closed to the open position between 80% and 92.5% speed.

The General Electric LM2500, shown in Fig. 29, uses an IGV plus a very extensive set of VSVs on seven stages. Hence, it does not require bleed valves.

FIGURE 29

General Electric LM2500 Gas Turbine IGV/VSV Linkage
(Courtesy of Tom Van Hardeveld)

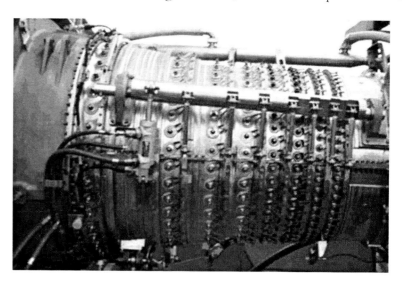

Compressor Blade Materials

Compressor blades operate at low or moderately high temperatures but are subject to high rotational stresses. Stator vanes and blades are often made from stainless or high alloy steel, or sometimes from titanium. They need to resist corrosion and erosion from external contaminants. Coatings are applied to increase compressor efficiency and reduce corrosion.

COMBUSTOR DESIGN

Combustors are designed to burn a wide variety of fuels — from natural gas to liquids, or even low energy gases. Some engines can use both natural gas and liquid fuel and switch from one to the other during operation. These systems require special fuel nozzles and more complicated fuel gas and control systems.

The combustion section must be able to burn a variety of fuels efficiently with low emissions, high reliability, and long life. Each fuel has an optimum set of combustion characteristics that must be met to give complete and efficient chemical reactions between the reactive elements in the fuel and oxygen in the air. The atmosphere in the combustor is very aggressive with combustion temperatures ranging from 900°C to 1850°C. The presence of oxides of sulphur and nitrogen creates a high potential for corrosion and erosion of the internal components. This requires the use of exotic alloys, ceramic coatings and sleeve cooling mechanisms to handle these conditions.

The temperature of combustion can reach 1850°C, but the temperature limit of most metals is closer to 1200°C. As a result, only about 20% of the air that flows through the combustion section is directly involved in combustion. The remaining 80%, called secondary air, is used to cool the combustion liner and dilute the air leaving the combustor to reduce its temperature before it reaches the turbine section.

Since combustion can only be sustained at fairly low velocities, combustion air is diffused at the inlet of the combustion section. This also helps increase air pressure. A vortex is maintained downstream from the fuel nozzles to provide the required velocity for sustained combustion. Then, the two air streams (combustion and secondary air) are mixed before leaving the combustor. This process is shown in Fig. 30. This is an example of a straight-through combustor design commonly used on aero-derivative engines because it minimizes the frontal area to reduce drag.

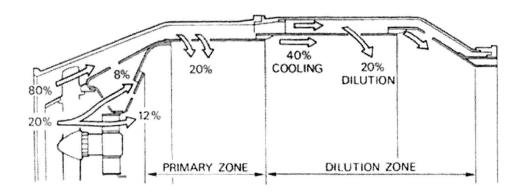

FIGURE 30

Air Flow in a Straight-Through Combustor
(Courtesy of Rolls Royce)

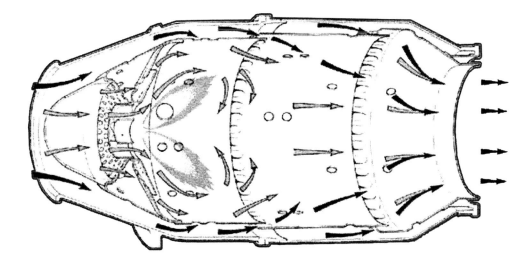

Many heavy-duty gas turbines use a reverse flow combustor, as shown in Fig. 31, to make the combustors more accessible. On startup, an igniter provides an electric spark to start the combustion process. Once started, combustion is self-sustaining. If the gas turbine has several combustors, more than one igniter may be installed. A crossfire tube, shown in Fig. 31, is used to ignite the other combustors and distribute the pressure evenly between combustors.

FIGURE 31

Air Flow through a Reverse-Flow Combustor
(Courtesy of GE Power Systems)

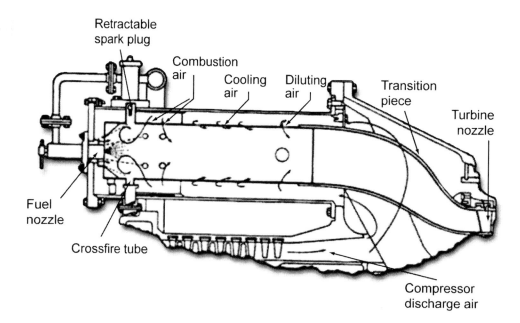

Types of Combustors

There are three basic combustor designs:
- Single-can (external)
- Annular
- Can-annular (turbo-annular)

Single-Can (External)

The single-can (Fig. 32) or external design combustor, often used on heavy-duty gas turbines, is usually reverse-flow combustors. Fig. 16 and Fig. 17 show gas turbines with external combustors.

Some gas turbines have only one, or sometimes two, main combustors (usually the reverse-flow type) mounted vertically above the turbine. This design can be seen in small gas turbines, such as the Kawasaki M1A-13A shown in Fig. 26.

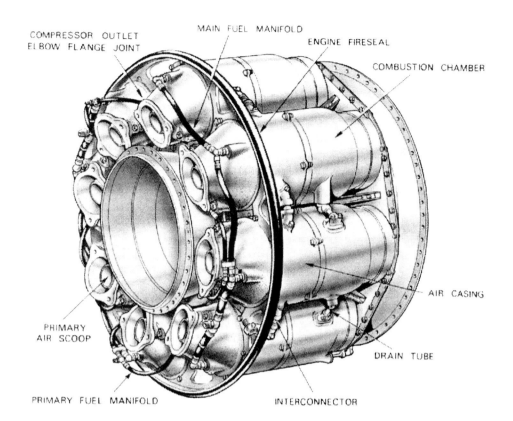

COMPRESSOR OUTLET
ELBOW FLANGE JOINT

MAIN FUEL MANIFOLD

ENGINE FIRESEAL

COMBUSTION CHAMBER

AIR CASING

PRIMARY
AIR SCOOP

DRAIN TUBE

PRIMARY FUEL MANIFOLD

INTERCONNECTOR

FIGURE 32

Single Can (External) Gas Turbine Combustor

Annular

The annular combustor (Fig. 33), a more modern concept, consists of a singular flame tube in an annular shape. It is smaller in size than the can burner and does not have the problem of combustion propagation between chambers. Combustion takes place in a single combustion liner, with an inner and outer casing, that encircles the centerline of the gas turbine. Fuel nozzles are evenly spaced around the ring. This is a very simple design that minimizes the complexity of the combustion and dilution air flows.

FIGURE 33

Annular Combustor

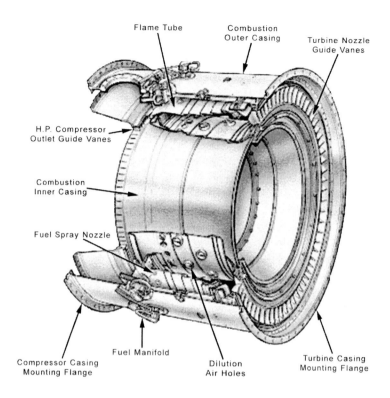

Fig. 34 shows the combustion and turbine sections of the General Electric LM2500. This engine uses an annular combustor design. Compressor air flows around the combustor to cool the liner and then the turbine discs downstream.

At the top is an optional design for dry low NO_x emission (discussed in Objective 10). This requires a different and larger combustor design with more fuel nozzles to reduce emissions.

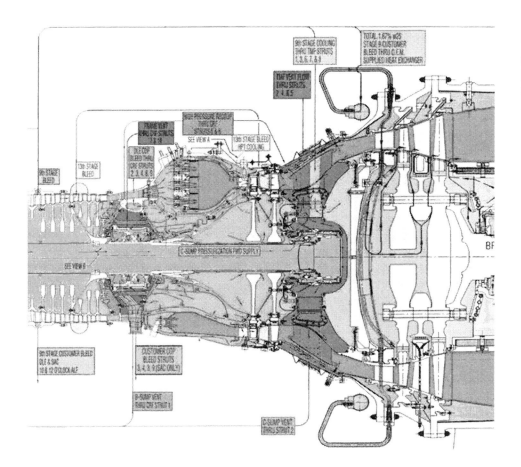

FIGURE 34

**General Electric
LM2500 Engine**
*(Courtesy of GE Power
Systems)*

Can-Annular (Turbo-annular)

In the can-annular or turbo-annular design combustor (Fig. 35), combustion takes place in multiple combustors (also called combustion cans) placed around the centerline of the gas turbine. Some aero-derivative gas turbines use this straight-through combustor design since it minimizes the front area of the turbine.

FIGURE 35

Can-Annular Combustor

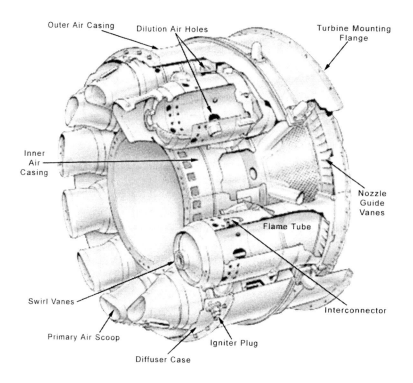

Combustor Liner Materials

Combustor liners are made from high-temperature nickel or cobalt-bases alloys such as Hastelloy® X and Mastelloy® X. These will usually be coated with ceramic coatings or tiles to improve their heat handling capacities. Some engines have combustors that are entirely ceramic, or ceramic mixed with high-temperature alloys. Special laser drilling techniques are used to precisely position the correct number and size of holes throughout the liner to allow for cooling air to flow in and give **film cooling** to the liner. As well, slots will be machined in the liner to allow the secondary air to enter the primary and dilution zones at just the right positions to:

- Stabilize the flame
- Assist in complete combustion
- Cool the combustion by-products

TURBINE DESIGN

After leaving the combustor, the hot gases are sent to the turbine section. Turbines operate at very high temperatures, high blade loading, and large rotational stresses. Like compressors, turbines can use either an axial-flow or a radial-inflow design, although axial-flow turbines are much more common.

In the reaction turbine, power is extracted from the hot gases exhausting from the combustors by experiencing an enthalpy reduction (pressure and temperature) through both the stationary and rotating blades which increases the velocity of the rotor. This power is first used to drive the internal compressor to make the gas turbine "self sustaining". The remaining energy is then used to drive process loads such as compressors, pumps or electrical power generators. As discussed in Objective 5, the hot gases may be passed through one or more turbine cylinders to extract all the available power. The turbine may use a number of different shaft arrangements to drive the various process loads.

Axial-flow Turbines

Because energy can be extracted more efficiently than it can be added, fewer stages are needed in the turbine than in the compressor. In axial flow turbines, a stage consists of a row of stationary blades (also called nozzle guide vanes or nozzles) followed by one or more rows of rotating blades depending on the type and design of the turbine. Nozzles increase the velocity of the hot gases with a partial pressure drop. Then, the moving blades extract power with a further drop in pressure and temperature.

The turbine section of the General Electric LM2500 is shown in Fig. 34. Note that a separate turbine drives the compressor, and a power turbine drives the generator, or other process loads. Cooling for the 2nd stage turbine nozzles is supplied from the 13th stage bleed valve. Cooling for the power turbine discs is supplied from the 9th stage bleed valve.

Blade Cooling

The current trend in gas turbine technology is to increase the inlet temperature of the gases, up to about 1370°C. This will increase the turbine power output as well as the turbine cycle efficiency. This increase has been achieved through advanced metallurgy and the use of special cooling systems for the turbine blades. Many gas turbines use air-cooled (or sometimes water-cooled) blades to reduce metal temperature and increase blade life. Air is supplied from the compressor discharge, circulated through the blade, and then extracted through holes in the leading edge, trailing edge, and surface of each blade.

The designs that are used for gas turbine cooling are:

- Film
- Transpiration
- Convection
- Impingement
- Water

Film

Cooling air is introduced through ports at the base of the blades where it then circulates through a series of vertical channels. The air passes out through a series of small holes bored in the blades leading edge. Slots are provided in the trailing edge to allow the escaping air to cool this part of the blade by convection. Film cooling is also used to protect the liners of the combustors from hot gases.

Transpiration

This type of cooling is achieved by passing air through the porous wall of the blades. At very high operating temperatures, this method is effective since the entire blade is covered with coolant flow. During normal operation, some of the pores are closed by oxidation. Consequently, this can cause uneven cooling and high thermal stresses. There can be a higher probability of blade failure when using this design.

Convection

Coolant air makes multiple passes through a serpentine channel from the hub to the tip, inside the turbine blade, to remove heat across the wall. This flow of air is in a radial direction. This is the most common type of cooling used in gas turbines.

Impingement

Jets of high velocity cooling air are blasted on the inner surface of the airfoil of the turbine blades. Heat transfer from the blade metal surface to the cooling air is increased. Since the leading edge of the blade requires more cooling than the midchord or trailing edge, the flow of cooling air is impinged at the leading edge.

Water

Preheated cooling water flows through a series of tubes that are embedded in the blade. The water absorbs heat and lowers the blade temperature below 540°C. It then discharges from the blade tip as steam into the gas stream.

An example of blade cooling is shown in Fig. 36. Air from the compressor section flows through the inside of the shaft into the nozzles and 1st stage rotor blades, which are hollow, and then escapes through the many cooling holes in the blades.

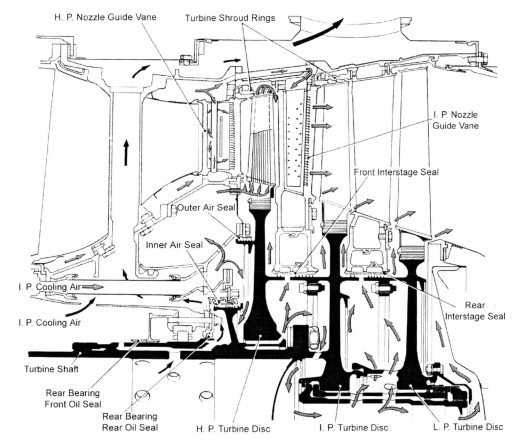

H. P. Nozzle Guide Vane

Turbine Shroud Rings

I. P. Nozzle Guide Vane

Front Interstage Seal

Outer Air Seal

Inner Air Seal

I. P. Cooling Air

I. P. Cooling Air

Rear Interstage Seal

Turbine Shaft

Rear Bearing Front Oil Seal

Rear Bearing Rear Oil Seal

H. P. Turbine Disc

I. P. Turbine Disc

L. P. Turbine Disc

FIGURE 36

Rolls Royce Avon Turbine Nozzle and Blade Cooling
(Courtesy of Rolls Royce)

Turbine Materials

One of the greatest challenges in gas turbine construction is selecting the materials to use in the turbine nozzles and blades, particularly for the first stage. Conventional nozzles and blades are cast from special nickel-based super alloys such as INCONEL®, UDIMET®, WASPALLOY™, and HASTELLOY® X. Special casting techniques are used to manufacture blades with superior strength and temperature resistance. Ceramic components will allow a significant increase in firing temperatures.

At very high temperatures and stresses, materials suffer from a phenomenon called creep. The material stretches over time which causes voids to open up. This can ultimately lead to catastrophic rupture and failure of the turbine blades.

Turbine blade life depends on the following items:
- Type of fuel burned
- Blade materials

- Operating conditions (number of stops and starts, loading percentages and temperature control)
- Ambient and environmental conditions

The first stage blade materials are the most important as they will experience the highest temperatures and the most corrosive conditions. These blades will last from 20 000 hours when burning residual oils to 100 000 hours when burning natural gas. Metallurgy used for the first stage blading is usually INCONEL (IN) 738 and their expected "life cycle" can be extended by coating the bladed with composite plasma or RT22. The second stage blades are made from precipitation-hardened nickel based alloys like U500 or nimonic. Nimonic is a nickel-chromium-cobalt alloy being precipitation hardenable, having high stress-rupture strength and creep resistance at high temperatures (up to about 950°C). It is a widely used and well proven alloy in high temperature conditions. The turbine wheels are made from Cr-Mo-V, 12 Cr alloys or M152.

AIR INTAKE SYSTEMS

The air intake system provides clean air to the gas turbine. To achieve this, air filters are installed in the intake. The type of air intake system used depends on the environmental conditions where the gas turbine is installed. Some environmental conditions that can greatly impact the type of air intake filtering systems installation are:

- Off-shore platform and ocean area installations
- Desert or high dust installations
- Cold climate and arctic installations
- High rain and wind conditions
- Industrial installations where their a number of sulphur compounds and corrosive materials in the local atmosphere

The intake system becomes more complicated if intake cooling (to increase power at high ambient temperatures) is required, or if icing conditions may occur.

An intake system is shown in Fig. 37. Note that the air intake is positioned above the enclosure to save space and to place the intake in a higher position where the air may be cleaner. The intake is designed to allow the installation of intake cooling or anti-icing.

The first stage of filtration is a stainless steel screen which prevents entry of major debris. The second stage is a series of cylindrical filters mounted inside the air intake which remove the bulk of the debris.

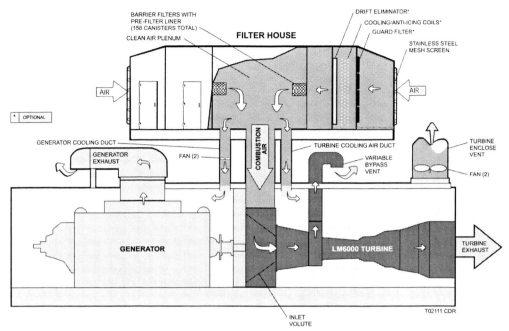

FIGURE 37

Air Intake System (GE LM6000)
(Courtesy of GE Power Systems)

Some filter systems use inertial filtering which consists of a series of vanes that deflect the air and separate the contaminants using centrifugal force. A more effective approach is to use many small cylindrical filters, such as the ones shown in Fig. 38. Compressed air is used to backflow individual filters and to dislodge dust that has been collected and deposited into a hopper or other type of removal system.

These pulse cleaning systems are commonly called **huff and puff** and operate automatically based on pressure differential. They work well in both dusty and cold weather conditions.

FIGURE 38

Pulse Cleaning Filter
(Courtesy of Donaldson)

Inlet Cooling

Inlet cooling systems decrease intake air temperature, and thereby increase power output, as shown in Fig. 39. A 0.5% decrease in power can result from a 1°C temperature increase. In hot climates, this variation in power output can be significant and costly. They are based on the principle of evaporative cooling. When moisture evaporates, it requires a large amount of heat to overcome the latent heat of vaporization. The result is a drop in air temperature.

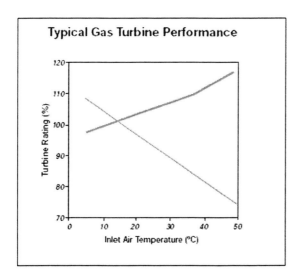

FIGURE 39

Typical Gas Turbine Performance

Various inlet cooling methods are used:

- Evaporative cooling
- Fog cooling
- Chillers

Evaporative Cooling

This system (Fig. 40) consists of a wetted media which is located downstream of the inlet air filter. This arrangement protects the wetted media from any airborne particles in the ambient air. Evaporative cooling enhances engine efficiency by increasing the density of the air. Increased air density raises the specific mass flow through the engine which improves the fuel efficiency and power output. This system operates as an air washer, thereby cleaning the air. Another advantage to this system is a reduction in the emissions of oxides of nitrogen.

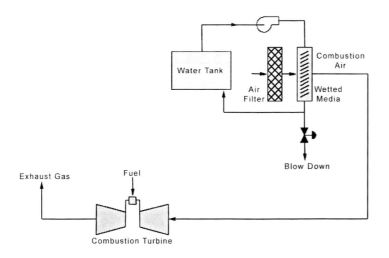

FIGURE 40

Evaporative Cooling

Fog Cooling

Atomized demineralized water under high pressure (7 000 to 20 000 kPa), is sprayed into an air steam (Fig. 41). Small fog droplets of approximately 10 microns (μm) diameter are desired as they have a faster evaporation rate. Fogging systems offer a very small pressure drop to the flow of inlet air to the gas turbine.

FIGURE 41

Fog Inlet Air Cooling System

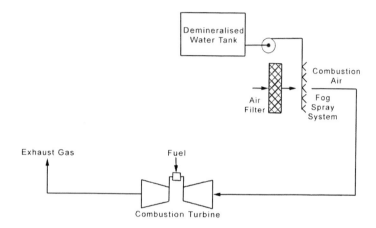

Chillers

Inlet air to the gas turbine is cooled by passing it through a finned coil of tubes (Fig. 42) which uses either NH_3 (Ammonia) or HFC-134a refrigerant as the cooling medium. The air temperature must not be less than 5°C to prevent the formation of ice on the coils. Refrigeration will always provide the design inlet temperature regardless of the ambient conditions, unlike the evaporative systems which lose effectiveness in high humidity conditions.

FIGURE 42

Refrigeration Air Cooling System

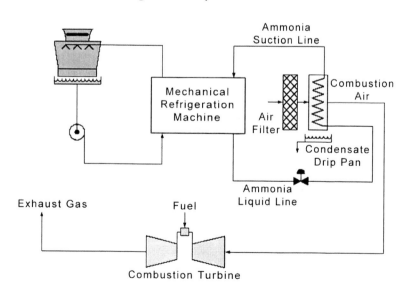

Anti-Icing Systems

Ice can form in the air intake, or on the first few stages of the compressor, when low temperatures combine with humidity. If chunks of ice are drawn into the compressor, they can cause major damage, such as catastrophic destruction of the compressor section blading.

Various anti-icing systems are used:
- Air is bled from the hot end of the compressor and injected into the front of the compressor through the nose cone and the first few stator vanes (see Fig. 43)
- Heating coils are installed in the air intake
- Heated air is fed from the exhaust (or another source) into the air intake

These systems are activated only when icing conditions are present because they reduce the efficiency and power output of the gas turbine.

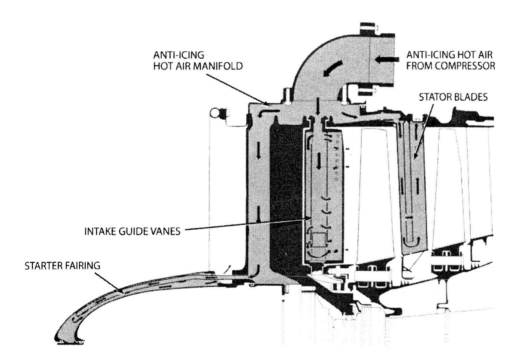

FIGURE 43

Rolls Royce Avon Anti-Icing System
(Courtesy of Rolls Royce)

EXHAUST SYSTEMS

The exhaust system directs the hot turbine exhaust, with as low a pressure loss as possible, to a location that is safe for employees and equipment. It has to be structurally sound and designed for high exhaust temperatures. Care should be taken to ensure that exhaust air does not re-circulate into the air intake since this will result in a loss of maximum power, unless this is part of an anti-icing system.

Noise attenuators and silencers are often added to the exhaust in accordance with local requirements.

GAS TURBINE LUBRICATING OIL SYSTEM

Most gas turbines have lube oil systems that lubricate the bearings supporting the rotor or rotors. Aero-derivative gas turbines use antifriction bearings which require small lube oil systems. Heavy-duty gas turbines use journal bearings which require larger lube oil systems. Microturbines are the exception; because of their small size, they are able to operate with air cooled bearings that do not require a lube oil system.

All lube oil systems perform the following basic functions:
- Lubricate and/or separate the rotating surfaces from the stationary surfaces
- Cool the bearings and other critical components
- Assist in controlling radial and axial thrust

All lube oil systems include these basic components:
- An oil reservoir to ensure an adequate supply of oil
- Oil heaters in the reservoirs to maintain a certain start-up temperature and reduce the potential for moisture to collect to collect in and contaminate the oil
- Filters to ensure the oil is clean
- Pumps to provide pressure
- Coolers to ensure oil temperatures are kept within operating limits
- Start-up permissives for oil pressure, oil temperature and oil flow rates
- Protective, monitoring, and control devices (*e.g.* gauges and safety valves)

Gas turbine installations may have one or more lube oil system. These are the major configurations:
- One integrated lube oil system that serves the gas turbine, power turbine, gearbox and driven equipment (compressor or generator), incorporated in heavy-duty gas turbines such as those manufactured by Solar Turbines.
- Two lube oil systems: one for the gas turbine and power turbine, one for the load device. This design is also used in heavy-duty gas turbines.

- Three separate lube oil systems: one for the engine, one for the power turbine, and one for the load. Used in some aero-derivative gas turbines.
- Bearings

Gas turbines use two different types of bearings:
- Antifriction (roller and/or ball) bearings - common in aero-derivative gas turbines that have lighter rotors
- Radial (journal or tilt-pad) bearings - common in heavy-duty gas turbines that have heavier rotors

Fig. 44 shows an antifriction (roller) bearing for a Rolls Royce RB211. It features a separate oil squeeze film to dampen the bearing and increase its life. This engine also uses ball bearings (not shown) to counter and control thrust.

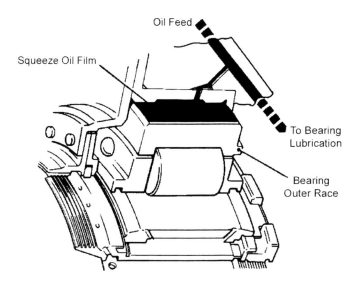

FIGURE 44

Rolls Royce RB211 Antifriction Bearing
(Courtesy of Rolls Royce)

The bearing configuration for the Rolls Royce RB211 is shown in Fig. 45. The two rotors shown require a more complicated arrangement using five bearings: two thrust (ball) bearings, and three roller bearings for the radial loads.

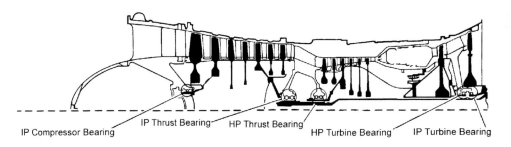

FIGURE 45

Rolls Royce RB211 Bearing Configuration
(Courtesy of Rolls Royce)

Heavy-duty gas turbines require radial bearings which can take higher loads. Although standard journal bearings are used, tilt-pad bearings are more common. Fig. 46 shows a Solar bearing with five tilting pads on individual pivot pins.

FIGURE 46

Radial Tilt-Pad Bearing
(Reprinted Courtesy of Solar Turbines Incorporated)

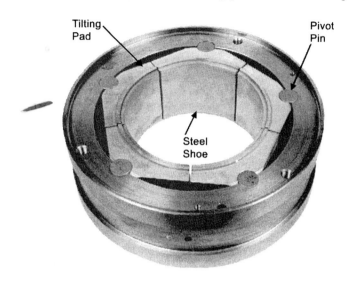

Fig. 47 shows a tilt-pad thrust bearing.

FIGURE 47

Tilt-Pad Thrust Bearing
(Reprinted Courtesy of Solar Turbines Incorporated)

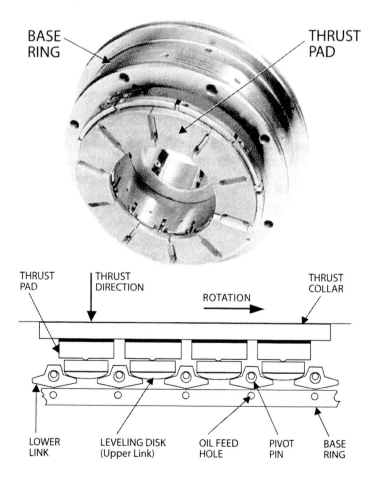

On a dual-shaft heavy-duty gas turbine, thrust bearings are located on the front end of the compressor, at the back end of the compressor, before the gas turbine, and after the power turbine. Thrust bearings are positioned at the front end of the compressor and next to the power turbine bearings (one for each shaft).

AERO-DERIVATIVE GAS TURBINE LUBE OIL SYSTEM

Fig. 48 shows the lube oil system for an aero-derivative gas turbine — the General Electric LM6000 (used for power generation). It lubricates the gas turbine and power turbine bearings. The driven equipment is handled by a separate system.

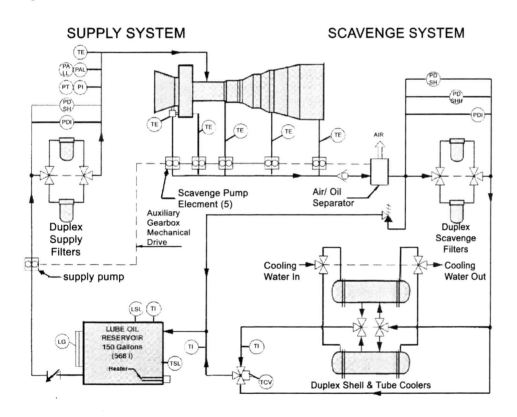

SUPPLY SYSTEM

SCAVENGE SYSTEM

FIGURE 48

General Electric LM6000 Lube Oil System
(Courtesy of GE Power Systems)

This lube oil system is divided into two sections: a supply system and a scavenge system. To prevent corrosion, all piping, fittings, and the reservoir are Type 304 stainless steel. The lube oil used is synthetic type oil suitable for high temperatures.

The oil reservoir contains approximately 500L in a 568L tank. It is fitted with protective devices to guard against low oil level and low oil temperature. A thermostatically controlled heater in the lube oil tank reservoir ensures that a minimum oil temperature is maintained to reduce the stresses on the turbine on startup and to keep moisture from condensing in the reservoir and contaminating the oil.

An electric motor driven auxiliary lube oil pump is used to initially pressurize the system and satisfy the permissives to allow the turbine to start.

A positive displacement pump, driven by an auxiliary gearbox on the engine, provides the required pressure to the bearings. After it leaves the pump, the oil is filtered through a duplex full-flow filter.

The oil supply is protected by switches for:

- High oil temperature
- Low oil pressure
- High filter differential pressure

Then, the oil flows through the bearings and accumulates in the bearing sumps. The oil temperature is measured at each scavenge line in case of bearing problems.

Chip detectors are often located in the sumps to detect metal particles. If a bearing becomes damaged, metal particles break away and become entrained in the oil. Chip detectors are basically magnets that attract metal particles and detect when they accumulate. When the chip detector alarms, the detector will be removed and the particles that have been captured by the detector will be analyzed. The quantity and type of material collected will indicate:

- Where the problem is
- How severe the problem has become

Scavenge pumps (also driven by the auxiliary gearbox) provide pressure to flow the oil from the bearing sumps through another set of filters, and then through duplex thermostatically controlled water-cooled coolers. Then, the oil flows back into the reservoir.

HEAVY-DUTY GAS TURBINE LUBE OIL SYSTEM

Fig. 49 shows the lube oil system for a heavy-duty gas turbine with a single integrated oil system serving the gas turbine, gearbox, and driven equipment.

The oil reservoir is much larger than aero-derivative gas turbine lube oil reservoirs. It normally contains mineral oil, which does not have as high a temperature range as synthetic oil, but is more cost-effective. Oil temperatures are not as high in heavy-duty gas turbines since the oil flow is greater. If necessary, equipment may be installed to heat the oil supply.

During normal operation, oil pressure is supplied by a main lube oil pump which is driven from an accessory drive mounted on the front of the compressor shaft. Prior to startup and on shutdown, oil pressure is supplied by an AC-driven pre/post lube oil pump. This pump runs for a period of time after shutdown to cool and lubricate the bearings and prevent damage. In case of power loss or pre/post lube oil pump failure, a third pump — using another source of energy, for example, a DC pump driven from batteries — is available as backup.

The cooled oil is cleaned by duplex filters that can be replaced during operation. Duplex filter systems consist of two filters in parallel to allow one to be serviced while the other is on line. It is monitored by a differential pressure alarm and pressure gauge. At the lube oil header, protection systems guard against high oil temperature and low oil pressure.

After leaving the bearings, the oil drains back into the oil reservoir using gravity. Oil temperature is usually measured in the drains to monitor bearing condition.

A hydraulic pump is sometimes installed after the main lube oil pump to supply high pressure oil to control the variable inlet and stator vanes, the fuel control valve, and bleed valves.

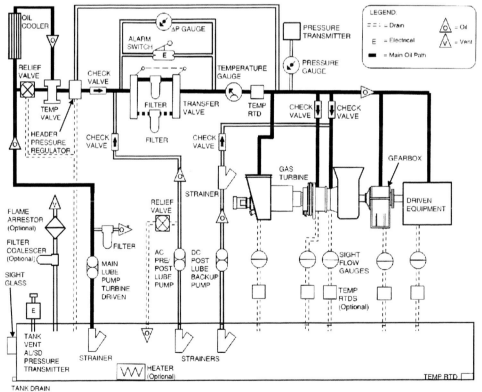

FIGURE 49

Lube Oil System for a Solar Gas Turbine
(Reprinted Courtesy of Solar Turbines Incorporated)

NATURAL GAS FUEL

Natural gas is the best fuel for gas turbines since it:
- Promotes the most efficient combustion
- Produces the lowest environmental emissions
- Delivers the longest engine life

It has to operate within a specified range of heating values and be free of liquid contaminants and sulphur compounds. The pressure of the turbine fuel gas system is usually much lower than the supply pipeline operating pressure. When the pressure is reduced across a throttling valve, the gas temperature will drop due to the natural refrigerating effect. This will tend to allow the heavier constituents in the gas to condense. For this reason, line heaters are usually installed just downstream of the pressure reducing valves to increase the gas temperature above the dew point of the heavier constituents in the gas.

If low energy fuel is used, special fuel nozzles and combustors must be installed. As well, the fuel gas system has to be adapted to accommodate the higher flow rates required to deliver the same fuel energy.

FUEL GAS SYSTEM

The General Electric LM6000 fuel gas system, shown in Fig.50, is representative of most gas turbines.

A fuel gas compressor is installed in case extra compression is required to boost a low pressure fuel source. The pressure of the fuel gas has to be higher than the pressure of the compressed air delivered to the combustion section. A pressure regulator and relief valve is installed to ensure that the fuel gas supply is maintained at the correct pressure. Low and high pressure switches protect against over or under pressure conditions.

A fuel filter ensures that contaminants do not enter the fuel system. Some systems use heat exchangers to raise the fuel gas to its optimum temperature to ensure that:
- Complete combustion occurs in the combustor
- The gas always remains above the dew point temperatures of the heaviest constituents in the fuel gas

A fuel gas flow meter monitors fuel consumption, but is not used for fuel control. Fuel is metered and controlled by the fuel metering valve, one of the most important components of the fuel gas system. It is also an essential component of the startup and shutdown sequence. Fuel valves are normally electrically controlled with hydraulic actuation, but electrically actuated valves are becoming more common. The fuel metering valve ensures that the correct amount of fuel is provided according to the operating conditions. It precisely controls the flow of fuel to ensure that maximum turbine temperature is not exceeded. The rate at which the fuel valve is opened and closed is limited to prevent temperature increases that might damage the turbine. Additional shutoff valves are provided for emergency purposes.

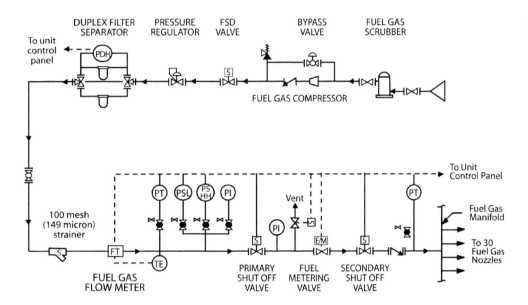

FIGURE 50

General Electric LM6000 Fuel Gas System
(Courtesy of GE Power Systems)

LIQUID FUELS

Gas turbines can burn a wide range of liquid fuels including:

- Distillates, such as kerosene, which do not require fuel treatment
- Blended heavy distillates and low ash crudes which require some treatment
- Residuals and heavy ash crudes which require considerable cleaning and treatment

Fuel quality affects gas turbine availability. As fuel quality decreases, maintenance actions and overhauls are needed more frequently and maintenance costs increase.

FUEL OIL SYSTEM

An example of a fuel oil system is shown in Fig. 51. The system starts with a fuel storage tank and fuel treatment.

Treatment varies with the type of fuel and may include centrifuges, filters, de-watering, and chemical treatment. Chemicals that are especially harmful to the turbine section are sodium, potassium, and vanadium since they cause rapid corrosion. Gas turbines burn mainly natural gas and light oil. Crude oil, residual, and some distillates contain corrosive components and as such require fuel treatment equipment. In addition, ash deposits from these fuels result in gas turbine deratings of up to 15 percent. However, they may still be economically attractive fuels, particularly in combined-cycle plants.

Sodium and potassium are removed from residual, crude and heavy distillates by a water washing procedure. A simpler and less expensive purification system will do the same job for light crude and light distillates. A magnesium additive system may also be needed to reduce the corrosive effects if vanadium is present. Fuels requiring such treatment must have a separate fuel-treatment plant and a system of accurate fuel monitoring to assure reliable, low-maintenance operation of gas turbines.

Then, the cleaned and treated oil is filtered and pumped to the gas turbine where it is filtered once more. Similar to fuel gas systems, there is a main metering valve with a primary and secondary shutoff valve. The liquid fuel must be supplied to the nozzles at a specific pressure to ensure proper and efficient atomization and combustion. To handle load changes the pressure controlled bypass valve directs the excess flow back to the storage tank to maintain a set operating pressure on the system. Drains are provided on the fuel manifolds.

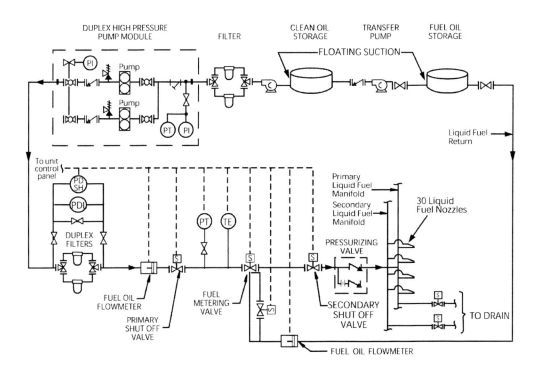

FIGURE 51

Liquid Fuel System (General Electric LM6000)
(Courtesy of GE Power Systems)

Protective instrumentation is installed on the fuel gas system to monitor, control, alarm and/or completely shutdown the unit for specific conditions of pressure, temperature and flow rates.

Dual Fuel Systems

Some gas turbines have dual fuel capability so that the operator can switch to a less expensive fuel, or use the alternative fuel as a backup. An example of a dual fuel system (gas and liquid), shown in Fig. 52, requires a special fuel nozzle. The control system design is more complex to manage the two types of fuels and to accommodate the switchover between them. Some systems can burn a mixture of gaseous and liquid fuels simultaneously.

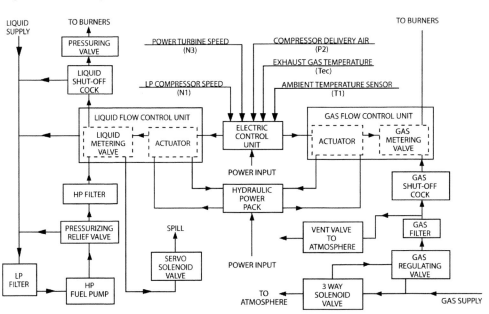

FIGURE 52

Dual Fuel System (Rolls Royce Avon)
(Courtesy of Rolls Royce)

STEAM OR WATER INJECTION SYSTEM

Gas turbines are required to produce low levels of emissions since the levels and types of emission are legislated and enforced in many areas. These increasingly stringent requirements have resulted in major changes to gas turbine design, particularly the combustion section.

Gas turbine emissions are summarized in Table 1. They are divided into two groups, major species, and minor species. Major species are measured in percent (%), while minor species are measured in parts per million (ppm). The specific pollutants produced depend on the operating conditions of the gas turbine, especially the combustion characteristics, and the type of fuel used.

TABLE 1

Gas Turbine Emissions
(Courtesy of GE Power Systems)

Major Species	Typical Concentration (% Volume)	Source
Nitrogen (N_2)	66 - 72	Inlet Air
Oxygen (O_2)	12 - 18	Inlet Air
Carbon Dioxide (CO_2)	1 - 5	Oxidation of Fuel Carbon
Water Vapor (H_2O)	1 - 5	Oxidation of Fuel Hydrogen
Minor Species Pollutants	**Typical Concentration (PPMV)**	**Source**
Nitric Oxide (NO)	20 - 220	Oxidation of Atmosphere Nitrogen
Nitrogen Dioxide (NO_2)	2 - 20	Oxidation of Fuel-Bound Organic Nitrogen
Carbon Monoxide (CO)	5 - 330	Incomplete Oxidation of Fuel Carbon
Sulfur Dioxide (SO_2)	Trace - 100	Oxidation of Fuel-Bound Organic Sulfur
Sulfur Trioxide (SO_3)	Trace - 4	Oxidation of Fuel-Bound Organic Sulfur
Unburned Hydrocarbons (UHC)	5 - 300	Incomplete Oxidation of Fuel or Intermediates
Particulate Matter Smoke	Trace - 25	Inlet Ingestion, Fuel Ash, Hot-Gas-Path
		Attrition, Incomplete Oxidation of Fuel or
		Intermediates

The focus of emission control efforts has been sulphur dioxides (SO_x) and nitrogen oxides (NO_x). Sulphur dioxides are formed from the burning of fossil fuels.

Nitrogen oxides are formed from the:
- Oxidation of free nitrogen already in the air by the high temperature of combustion
- Partial combustion of fossil fuels

In general, the formation of NO_x can be managed by reducing flame temperature. The four methods of NO_x control are:
- Water injection
- Dry low NO_x emission combustor design
- Catalytic reduction
- Lean pre-mixed combustion

WATER INJECTION SYSTEMS

The earliest methods to reduce NO_x emissions involved the injection of water or steam into the combustor. This approach has been applied mainly to heavy-duty gas turbines and less frequently to aero-derivative gas turbines. Water or steam injection can reduce NO_x levels to 25 ppm_v (parts per million per volume) for natural gas fuels from normal levels of 150 - 200 ppm_v without emission control.

Water is also used to reduce NO_x emissions from oil-fired combustion systems. It is mixed with the oil before being sprayed into the burner. Water decreases the combustion temperature and can reduce NO_x emissions from burning light weight oils by as much as 15%. A significant added advantage in using these emulsions is that they reduce the emission of particulate matter. When water is mixed in the oil, each oil droplet sprayed into the firebox has several tiny water droplets inside. The heat existing in the firebox makes these water droplets flash into steam and explode the oil droplet. Increasing the surface area of the oil enables it to burn faster and more completely. A reduction in particulate emissions can be achieved regardless of whether light or heavy oils are being burned.

Emissions are reduced by introducing a heat sink to limit flame temperature. An additional benefit is that power output is increased due to an increase in the mass flow. Water is more effective than steam, not only because it is at a lower temperature, but also due to the latent heat of vaporization. In fact, about 1.6 times the amount of steam is required to produce the same effect.

The major limitation is that the quality of the water must be very high, similar to boiler feed water, to reduce deposits and corrosion in the downstream hot gas path components. Since a substantial amount of water is required, this method is not suitable for many situations.

Water is injected directly into the combustor by one of two methods:
- Water injection fuel nozzle
- Breech-load fuel nozzle

Water Injection Fuel Nozzle

Water is injected using water spray nozzles (Fig. 53) installed close to each fuel injector. Water injection systems require a water pump and filters, flow meters, water stop, and flow control valves, in addition to a more complicated control system. Steam injection systems require a steam flow meter, steam control valve, steam stop valve, and steam blowdown valves.

FIGURE 53

Water Injection Fuel Nozzle
(Courtesy of GE Power Systems)

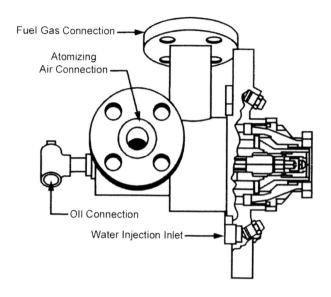

Breech-Load Fuel Nozzle

Fig. 54 shows a breech-load fuel nozzle where the water is injected in one spot upstream of the combustors to allow for premixing with the fuel before combustion.

FIGURE 54

Breech-load Fuel Nozzle
(Courtesy of GE Power Systems)

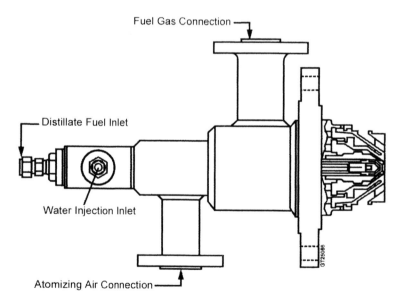

DRY LOW NO$_X$ EMISSION COMBUSTOR DESIGN

Development started in the 1970's to produce an emission control system that did not use water or steam and could also achieve lower emission levels. This method is usually known as either dry low NO$_x$ (DLN) or dry low emission (DLE) depending on the manufacturer. Levels, as low as 7ppm$_v$, are now being achieved in large industrial gas turbines.

Dry emission systems are based on the fact that emission of NO$_x$ is drastically reduced if the air-fuel mixture is lean or less than stoichiometric (the correct proportion of air to fuel required to achieve total combustion). The disadvantage with lean mixtures is that combustion becomes unstable, especially at part load.

Various designs have been developed to provide stable operation, some of which use a series of staged fuel nozzles. An example of this design, used in heavy-duty gas turbines, is shown in Fig. 55. It features two sets of fuel nozzles:

- Primary fuel nozzle for startup and part load operation
- Secondary nozzle for lean operation and lowest emissions at full load

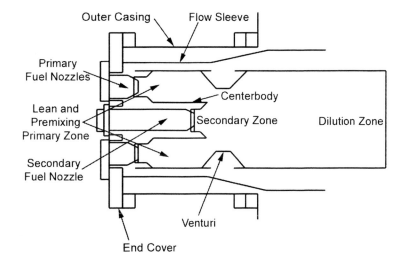

FIGURE 55

Dry Low NOx Combustor
(Courtesy of GE Power Systems)

The staging of these nozzles is shown in Fig. 56.

FIGURE 56

Fuel-Staged Dry Low NOx Operating Modes
(Courtesy of GE Power Systems)

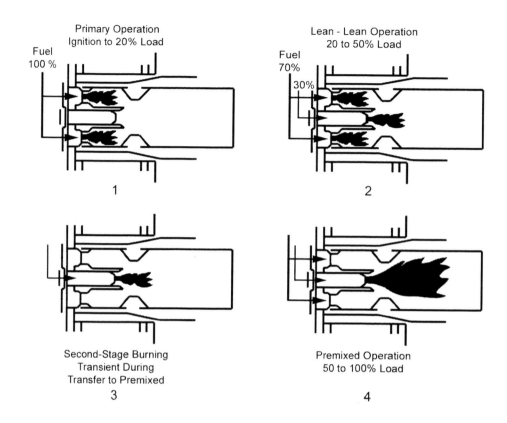

CATALYTIC REDUCTION

NO$_x$ emissions are removed from the burner exhaust gases through the use of a catalyst. In one process, ammonia is added to the flue gas prior to the gas passing over a catalyst. The catalyst enables the ammonia to react chemically with the NO$_x$ converting it to molecular nitrogen and water. The catalyst used is a combination of titanium and vanadium oxides. This system promotes the removal of up to 90% of nitrogen oxides from the flue gases.

The ammonia reacts with both the nitrogen monoxide (NO) and nitrogen dioxide (NO$_2$)

Reaction with NO:

$$4NO + 4NH_3 + O_2 = 4N_2 + 6H_2O$$

Reaction with NO$_2$:

$$2NO_2 + 4NH_3 + O_2 = 3N_2 + 6H_2O$$

The NO and NO_2 react with the ammonia to form nitrogen and water. The nitrogen is harmless and can be released back into the atmosphere.

In a second process, both NO_x and SO_x are removed. The combustion gases are passed across a bed of copper oxide, which reacts with the sulphur oxide to form copper sulphate. The copper sulphate acts as a catalyst for reducing NO_x to ammonia. Approximately 90% of the NO_x and SO_x can be removed from the flue gases through this process.

LEAN PRE-MIXED COMBUSTION

Another method of reducing the formation of NO_x is to reduce the flame temperature by thoroughly premixing the fuel with large quantities of air prior to combustion. Referring to Fig. 57, in a conventional gas turbine combustor, 30% of the total air flow is mixed with the fuel supply to the burner. The remaining 70% of the required air flow is added at later stages to the burner. This results in a burner temperature of approximately 2260°C.

With the Solar Turbine SoLoNOx® type of burner, 60% of the total air flow is mixed with the fuel supply to the burner. The remaining 40% is added at later stages. This results in a burner temperature of 1590°C. This lean-premixed combustion technology ensures a uniform air/fuel mixture and prevention of the formation of NO_x.

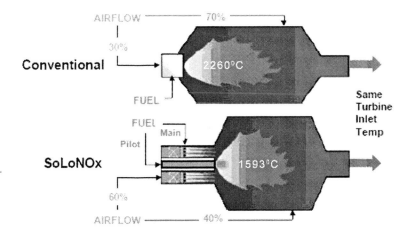

FIGURE 57

Lean Pre-Mixed Combustion Design *(Courtesy of Solar Turbines)*

Gas Turbine Auxiliaries and Operation

Here is what you will be able to do when you complete each objective:

1. Describe the types of bearings used in a gas turbine and explain the components, operation, protective devices and routine maintenance of a typical lube oil system.

2. Describe and explain the operation and routine maintenance of a typical fuel gas supply system for a gas turbine.

3. Describe and explain the operation and routine maintenance of a typical fuel oil supply system for a gas turbine.

4. Explain the control of NO_X from a gas turbine and describe the purpose and operation of water/steam injection and dry low NO_X systems.

5. Explain the purpose, location and operation of the gas turbine starting motor and turning gear.

6. Describe the compressor intake and the turbine exhaust components.

7. Describe the preparation and complete start-up sequence for a gas turbine.

8. Describe the shutdown sequence and procedure for a gas turbine.

9. Explain the purpose and describe typical on-line and off-line waterwash procedures for gas turbine blades.

LUBE OIL SYSTEMS

Almost all gas turbines have a lube oil system that lubricates the bearings that support the rotor or rotors. Aero-derivative gas turbines normally use antifriction bearings which require only a small lube oil system. Heavy-duty gas turbines use radial bearings that necessitate a larger lube oil system. Microturbines are an exception and, because of their small size, are able to operate with air bearings that do not require a lube oil system.

Gas turbine installations may have more than one lube oil system. These are the major configurations:

- Some heavy-duty gas turbines, such as those manufactured by Solar Turbines, have a single integrated lube oil system that serves the gas turbine, power turbine, gearbox and driven equipment (compressor or generator)

- Other heavy-duty gas turbines have a lube oil system for the gas turbine and power turbine but incorporate a separate lube oil system for the load device

- Most aero-derivatives require separate lube oil systems for the engine and for the power turbine and load

All lube oil systems provide two basic functions:

- Lubricate sliding surfaces in the bearings

- Cool the bearings; especially those located close to the combustion and turbine sections of the gas turbine

All oil systems consist of these basic components:

- An oil reservoir to ensure an adequate supply of oil

- Filters to ensure the oil is clean
- Pumps to provide pressure

- Coolers to ensure oil temperatures are kept within operating limits

- Protective, monitoring and control devices

BEARINGS

Gas turbines use two different types of bearings:

- Antifriction (roller and/or ball) bearings which are common in aero-derivative gas turbines because rotors are light enough

- Radial (journal or tilt-pad) bearings for heavy-duty gas turbines that have heavier rotors

Fig. 1 illustrates an antifriction (roller) bearing. It features a special squeeze film to dampen the bearing and increase its life. This engine also uses ball bearings for thrust.

FIGURE 1

Rolls Royce Antifriction Bearing
(Courtesy of Rolls-Royce plc)

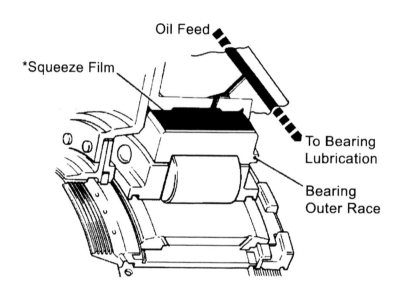

The antifriction bearing has two shafts (rotors) and uses a total of five bearings — two thrust (ball) bearings and three radial loads (roller) bearings.

Heavy-duty gas turbines require bearings, which can take higher loads. Although standard journal bearings have been used in the past, the most common type of radial bearing used today is the tilt-pad bearing. Fig. 2 shows a bearing which has five tilting pads on individual pivot pins. A tilt-pad thrust bearing can be seen in Fig. 3. On a typical dual-shaft heavy-duty gas turbine, bearings will be located on the front end of the compressor, at the end of the compressor, before the turbine and after the power turbine. Thrust bearings will be positioned at the front end of the compressor and next to the power turbine bearings (one for each shaft).

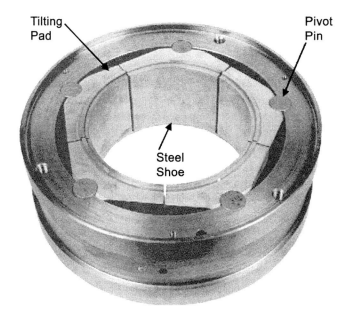

Tilting Pad

Pivot Pin

Steel Shoe

FIGURE 2

Typical Radial Tilt-Pad Bearing
(Solar Turbines)

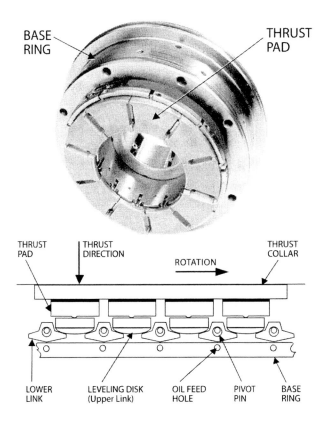

BASE RING

THRUST PAD

THRUST PAD   THRUST DIRECTION   ROTATION   THRUST COLLAR

LOWER LINK   LEVELING DISK (Upper Link)   OIL FEED HOLE   PIVOT PIN   BASE RING

FIGURE 3

Typical Tilt-Pad Thrust Bearing (Solar Turbines)

Aero-Derivative Gas Turbine Lube Oil System

Fig. 4 shows a typical lube oil system for an aero-derivative gas turbine used for power generation. It lubricates the bearings of both turbine sections – the compressor turbine and the power turbine. The lubrication of the load (driven) equipment is handled by a separate system.

This oil system is divided into two sections: a supply system and a scavenge system. The scavenge system returns the oil from the bearings to the supply and treating equipment. All piping, fittings and reservoir are Type 304 Stainless Steel to prevent corrosion. The system uses synthetic oil suitable for high temperatures.

The oil reservoir contains approximately 130 gal. in a 150 gal. tank. Protection devices are fitted against low oil level and low oil temperature. A thermostatically controlled heater is included and ensures a minimum temperature is maintained while the unit is not operating, to facilitate easy starting.

A positive displacement pump driven by an auxiliary gearbox on the engine provides the required pressure to the bearings. After the pump, the oil is filtered by a duplex, full flow filter that allows filter changeout while running. The oil supply is protected by high oil temperature, low oil pressure and high filter differential pressure switches.

FIGURE 4

Typical Lube Oil System
(General Electric)

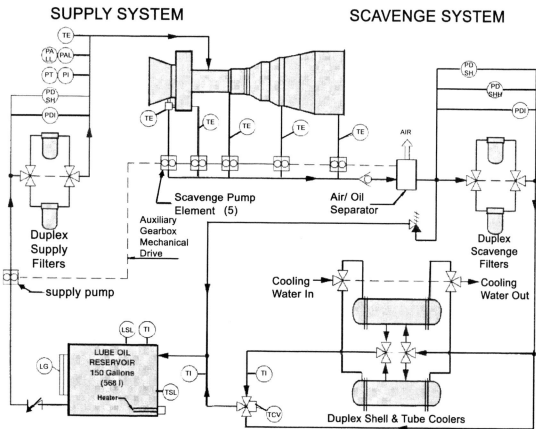

The oil flows through the bearings and accumulates in the bearing sumps. The oil temperature is measured at each scavenge line in case of bearing problems.

Chip detectors are often located in the sumps to detect metal particles from the bearings. If a bearing becomes damaged, metal particles will become entrained in the oil. The chip detector is basically a magnet that attracts these metallic particles and detects when they accumulate on the magnet. Upon alarm, the detector is removed and inspected to diagnose the type and extent of bearing damage.

Scavenge pumps, also driven by the auxiliary gearbox of the turbine, provide the pressure for the oil to flow through another set of filters and then through duplex, water-cooled coolers that are thermostatically controlled. The oil then flows back to the reservoir.

Heavy-Duty Gas Turbine Lube Oil System

The lube oil system shown in Fig. 5 is typical for a heavy-duty gas turbine with one integrated oil system for the gas turbine, gearbox and driven equipment.

FIGURE 5

Lube Oil System for a Typical Gas Turbine

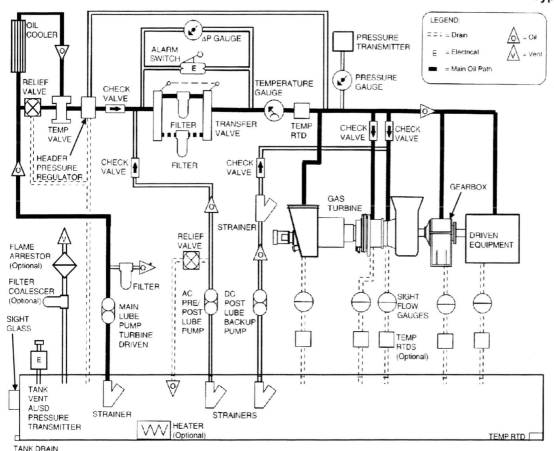

The oil reservoir is much larger than for aero-derivative gas turbines. It normally contains mineral oil, which does not have as high a temperature capability as synthetic oil, but is more economic. Generally, oil temperatures are not as high in heavy-duty gas turbines since the oil flow is greater. Oil heating may be supplied if required.

Oil pressure is supplied during normal operation by a main lube oil pump driven from the accessory drive mounted on the front of the compressor shaft. Prior to startup and on shutdown, oil pressure is supplied by a motor driven pre/post lube oil pump. This pump runs for a period of time after shutdown to cool and lubricate the bearings and prevent damage. A third pump using another source of energy (for example a direct current motor supplied by batteries) is available as backup in case of power loss or pre/post lube oil pump failure.

The oil is cleaned with duplex filters that allow filter replacement during operation. There is a differential pressure alarm and pressure gauge. The oil is then cooled prior to entering the bearings by either an air or water cooler. At the lube oil header, there is protection against high oil temperature and low oil pressure.

The oil drains back into the oil reservoir using gravity. The oil temperature is also normally measured in the drains to monitor bearing health.

Hydraulic System

A hydraulic pump is sometimes provided after the main lube oil pump to supply high pressure oil for the actuation of the main turbine instrumentation for controlling speed and load. The location of the connection for this point is shown in Fig. 5 by an asterisk (*), located just after a filter branching off of the main lube oil line, immediately downstream of the main lube pump. The hydraulic system is typically the medium through which the turbine speed sensor sends its signal to the speed control valve that modulates the fuel flow to the turbine, as well as to the variable inlet and stator vanes, and bleed valves.

Oil System Maintenance

Oil systems are relatively maintenance free and automatic protection is usually provided against common problems. Maintenance consists of:

- Checking for oil leaks (usually daily)

- Monitoring oil pressures and temperatures (usually daily)

- Checking chip detectors when they alarm

- Topping up the oil reservoir or secondary lube oil tank. Often the reservoir is kept filled by a second supply tank with an automatic slow fill valve and level control.

- Changing oil filters when the differential pressure alarms

- Cleaning the cooler externally

- Taking oil samples regularly for analysis and replacing oil when required

- Calibrating instrumentation and testing protective devices

System temperatures and pressures, and the status of pumps, filters and coolers, are usually monitored and displayed on computer screens. This type of interface may also be used to start or stop the lubrication and hydraulic system pumps.

NATURAL GAS FUEL

Natural gas is the best fuel for gas turbines since it promotes the most efficient combustion and produces the lowest environmental emissions. Engine life is also the longest with clean natural gas. It has to be within a specified range of heating values and be free of liquid contaminants. Natural gas is often heated to ensure no liquids are present. If fuel with a low energy value is used, special fuel nozzles and combustors have to be installed and the fuel gas system has to be adapted because of the corresponding requirement for higher flow rates.

FUEL GAS SYSTEM

The fuel gas system shown in Fig. 6 is typical for most gas turbines.

FIGURE 6

Typical Fuel Gas System (General Electric)

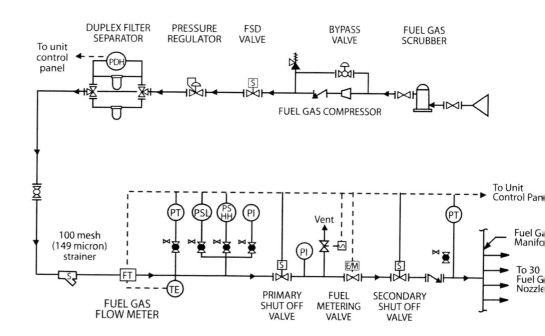

A fuel gas compressor is shown in case extra compression is required to boost a low pressure fuel source. The pressure of the fuel gas has to be higher than the compressed air delivered to the combustion section. A pressure regulator and relief valve are also installed to ensure steady fuel pressures at the combustor. Low and high pressure switches protect against over or under pressure conditions.

A fuel filter is then installed to ensure contaminants do not enter the fuel system. Some systems also have a heat exchanger to remove liquids and increase fuel temperature to required levels.

A fuel gas flow meter is installed to enable the determination of fuel consumption but is otherwise not needed for fuel control.

The fuel flow rate is measured and controlled by the fuel metering valve which is the most important component of the fuel gas system. It ensures that the right amount of fuel is provided for the operating conditions. It is precisely controlled to ensure that the maximum turbine temperature is not exceeded. It is an essential component of the startup and shutdown sequence. The rate at which the fuel valve is opened or closed is also limited to prevent temperature increases that might damage the turbine. Additional shutoff valves are provided for emergency purposes.

Fig 7 shows a typical fuel valve. They are normally electrically controlled with hydraulic actuation but electrically actuated valves are starting to become common.

FIGURE 7

Typical Fuel Gas Metering Valve (General Electric)

ROUTINE MAINTENANCE

Fuel gas systems are relatively maintenance free and automatic protection is usually provided against common problems. Maintenance consists of:

- Checking for fuel gas leaks (usually daily)

- Monitoring pressures and temperatures (usually daily)

- Changing fuel filters at the required differential pressure

- Calibrating instrumentation and testing protective devices

Fig. 8 shows a typical computer control system display used for monitoring a fuel system. Since the unit is stopped, the valves are in the closed position except for the vent valves. The 310 valve is a pressure regulator, the 20F12 valve is the main shutoff valve and the 65BA valve is the fuel metering valve.

FIGURE 8

**Monitoring Screen for
the Fuel Gas Control
System**
*(Courtesy of Rolls-
Royve plc)*

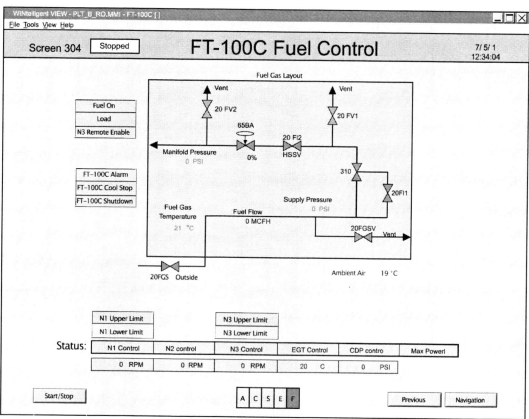

LIQUID FUELS

The gas turbine can operate on a wide range of liquid fuels including:

- Distillates, such as kerosene, for which no fuel treatment is required

- Blended heavy distillates and low ash crudes, which require some treatment

- Residuals and heavy ash crudes that require considerable cleaning and treatment

The life of the gas turbine (in terms of time between maintenance actions and overhauls) is reduced as the quality of the fuel decreases. Maintenance costs increase as well.

FUEL OIL SYSTEM

A typical fuel oil system is shown in Fig. 9. The system starts with a fuel storage tank and fuel treatment.

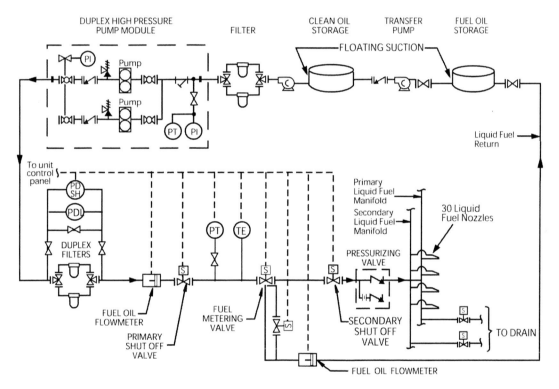

FIGURE 9

Typical Liquid Fuel System
(General Electric)

Treatment varies with the type of fuel and may include centrifuges, filters, dewatering and chemical treatment. Chemicals that are especially harmful to the turbine section are sodium, potassium and vanadium since they cause rapid corrosion.

The cleaned and treated oil is then filtered and pumped to the gas turbine where it is filtered once more. There is a main metering valve with a primary and secondary shutoff valve. At the fuel metering valve, there is an overflow for unused fuel back to the fuel tank. Drains are provided on the fuel manifolds.

Protective instrumentation is installed for filter differential pressure and low pressure.

Dual Fuel Systems

Some gas turbine installations feature dual fuel capability so that the operator can switch to a less expensive fuel or as a backup. An example of a dual fuel system is shown in Fig. 10. Liquid fuel is shown entering at the top left of the system, and fuel gas at the lower right. The electronic control unit in the centre of the system selects which metering and control system (liquid or gas) will be in operation, and therefore which fuel will be sent to the burners. A special fuel nozzle is required and the control system is more complex to manage the two types of fuels and to accommodate the switchover between them. With some systems, a mixture of gaseous and liquid fuels can be burned simultaneously.

FIGURE 10

Typical Dual Fuel System
(Courtesy of Rolls Royve plc)

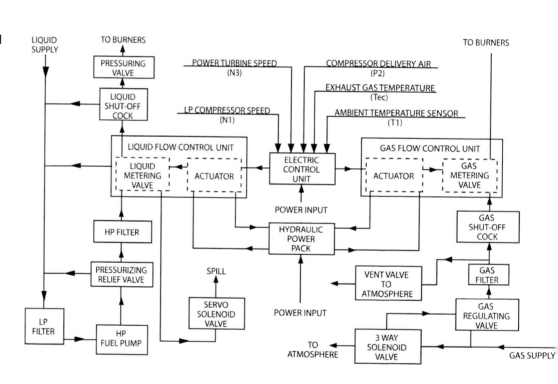

ROUTINE MAINTENANCE

Fuel oil systems are relatively maintenance free and automatic protection is usually provided against common problems. If specialized fuel treatment is required (for example when waste products are being used as fuel sources) more maintenance is generally required.

Maintenance consists of:

- Checking for fuel oil leaks (usually daily)

- Monitoring pressures and temperatures (usually daily)

- Cleaning centrifuges and other treatment components and replenishing chemicals

- Changing fuel filters at the required differential pressure

- Calibrating instrumentation and testing protective devices.

NOX EMISSIONS

NO_X refers to a family of compounds – NO and NO_2. They are formed during combustion from the reaction of the oxygen and nitrogen naturally occurring in the air, and are partially responsible for creating acid rain. As can be seen in Fig. 11, the rate of NO_X formation decreases exponentially as the temperature decreases. The main way to decrease NO_X is to decrease the fuel to air ratio and operate with a lean fuel mixture. However, a decrease in combustion temperature also increases the undesirable formation of CO (carbon monoxide) so a balance has to be achieved.

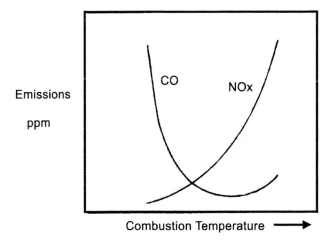

FIGURE 11

Dependence of NOx on Combustion Temperature

WATER OR STEAM INJECTION SYSTEMS

Water or steam injection reduces NO_x by dropping the combustion temperature, which drastically reduces the formation of NO_x. Either steam or water can be used depending on what is most easily available. Cleanliness and purity of the water or steam is of paramount importance to prevent corrosion of hot section components.

The water or steam can be injected into the combustion section through the fuel nozzles or can be premixed with liquid fuels in a separate manifold.

Aside from increased corrosion, the main disadvantage of water or steam injection is that, as more water or steam is injected to further reduce NO_x, the thermal efficiency is reduced because of the energy transferred to the water or steam. There is also an increase in combustion activity and pulsation, which reduces the life of hot section components. There is, however, an increase in power output that is important to some users.

The practical limit for NO_x emissions achievable with water or steam injection is 25 ppm for natural gas and 42 ppm for liquid fuels.

DRY LOW NO_x COMBUSTION SYSTEMS

The standard scrubbing method for limiting NO_x is now mostly being replaced by dry low NO_x (DLN for dry low NO_x or DLE for dry low NO_x emission) technology, which is able to achieve the lower levels now required. The standard maximum level for NO_x in many locations is now 25 ppm and some gas turbines are now able to reach levels of 9 ppm.

Dry low NO_x combustion systems operate on the principle of lean premixed combustion. Air and fuel are premixed to the proper lean proportion and then combusted at lower temperatures. This requires an increase in combustion area. Fig. 12 shows a DLE configuration. Instead of single fuel nozzles, a triple annulus arrangement is used. They are staged over the operation of the gas turbine so that only one is used at low speeds; another one is activated at medium load and the third one is added at maximum speeds. The extensive solenoid arrangement required to make this work can be seen in Fig. 12.

Other manufacturers use variations on this approach but the basic principles are the same. In all cases, fuel control becomes more complicated to enable low NO_x to be achieved over the entire operating envelope. Some vendors are also supplying retrofit options for existing equipment.

Catalytic systems, either during combustion or after a combined cycle exhaust heat exchanger, offer future possibilities for very low levels of emissions. However, they are still in the research and development stages and will not be commercially viable for some time to come.

FIGURE 12

Fuel Manifold and Solenoids for Low NOx Combustors
(General Electric)

STARTING SYSTEMS

Gas turbines must have a source of power (other than the compressor or load turbines) to provide the initial compression needed for ignition. This power source is used to rotate the large mass of the compressor, and bring it up to the speed necessary to supply combustion air to the combustor. The starting system engages the compressor shaft at the beginning of the start-up. Once ignition has been obtained, this system is disengaged from the compressor shaft. A variety of devices can be used to provide the initial rotation of the main compressor, including:

- pneumatic starters using compressed air or gas
- electric motors
- small diesel engines
- steam turbine expanders

Of these, pneumatic starters and electric motors are the most common.

Pneumatic Starters

High pressure air or gas can be expanded in a small turbine (called a starter motor) to drive the main gas turbine compressor up to ignition conditions. This is a particularly convenient system in remote gas pipeline applications (where the gas turbine itself is used to drive large transmission compressors). The high pressure pipeline gas is used as the starting gas supply.

Fig. 13 and 14 illustrate a pneumatic starter system. In this case a dual starter configuration is used. The user has the option of using air or gas depending on the most convenient source. The exhaust of the starter motor is normally vented to the atmosphere. The starter transmits power to the front end of the gas turbine rotor by means of an overrunning clutch. The shutoff valve is also pneumatically operated.

FIGURE 13

**Pneumatic Starter
System Diagram**

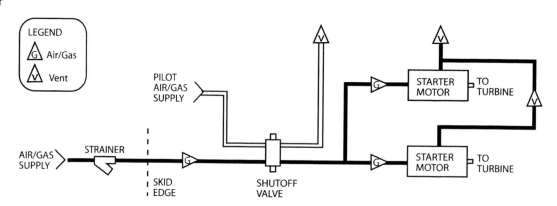

FIGURE 14

**Pneumatic Starter
Installation**

1 Clutch Lubrication Fixed Orifice (FO921)	3 Pneumatic Starter Motor (M922–1)
2 Gas Shutoff Pilot Solenoid Valve (L330–1)	4 Gas Shutoff Valve (V2P921)

Electric Starters

Electric starters consist of an ac motor and a variable frequency drive as shown in Fig. 15 and 16, but otherwise operate in the same fashion as a pneumatic starter. The variable frequency drive enables the motor speed to be controlled while still maintaining motor efficiency.

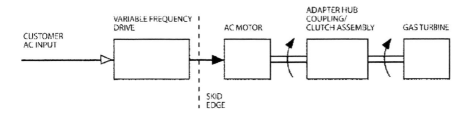

FIGURE 15

Electric Starter Diagram

FIGURE 16

Electric Starter Installation

TURNING GEAR

On larger gas turbines, especially of the heavy-duty type, the rotors are quite heavy and they develop a sag or bow when they cool down after shutdown. If a rotor becomes bowed, the rotor may lock and prevent startup or it may result in high vibration until the bow slowly disappears.

To prevent this, a special turning motor is provided to slowly turn the shaft for a number of hours after shutdown. This is sometimes a hydraulic ratchet or a slow turning electric motor. The motor and the turbine shaft have corresponding gears. The turning motor gear can be engaged or disengaged (normal turbine operation) with the shaft. A similar type of device is used on large steam turbines for their warm-up and cool-down periods.

AIR INTAKE SYSTEM

The air intake system ensures that clean air is provided to the gas turbine. To achieve this, air filters are installed in the intake to filter the air. The type of air intake system is dependent on the environmental conditions encountered at the gas turbine location. Special challenges are posed when a gas turbine is installed on an offshore platform, close to the ocean, in a desert or dusty location, or in an arctic environment. The intake system becomes more complicated if intake cooling (to increase power at high ambient temperatures) is required, or if icing conditions may occur.

A typical intake system is shown in Fig. 17. Note that in this design, the air intake is positioned above the enclosure both to save space and to place the intake in a higher position where the air may be cleaner. The intake is designed to allow the installation of intake cooling and/or anti-icing. The first stage of filtration is a stainless steel screen to prevent entry of major debris. The main filtration is achieved by a series of cylindrical filters mounted inside the air intake.

FIGURE 17

Typical Air Intake System
(General Electric)

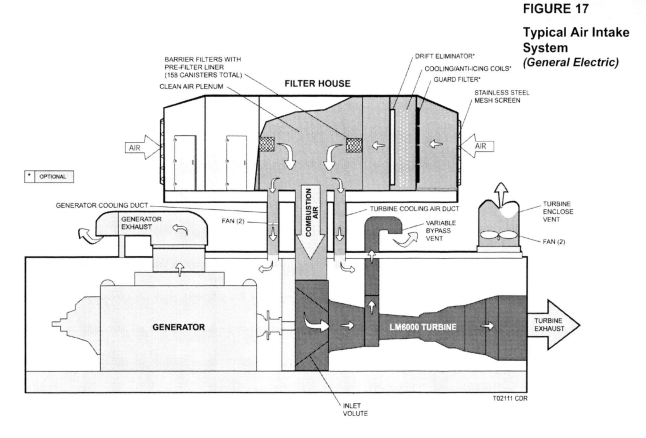

In the past, many filter systems were based on inertial filtering which consisted of a series of vanes that deflected the air to separate the contaminants, using centrifugal force. The current approach is to use many small cylindrical filters such as the ones shown in Fig. 18. In this system, compressed air is used to backflow individual filters and dislodge the dust that has collected on them. These "pulse cleaning systems" are commonly called "huff and puff", and operate automatically, based on pressure differential. They work well in both dusty and cold weather conditions.

FIGURE 18

Pulse Cleaning Filter
(Donaldson Company)

Inlet Cooling

Inlet cooling systems that decrease the temperature of the inlet air and thereby increase power output have been available for a long time but are now seeing renewed interest. They are based on the principle of evaporative cooling. When water evaporates, it requires a large amount of latent heat, which is provided by the warmer air. The result is a drop in air temperature.

Various methods are used today:

- Spray cooling where air is sprayed into the intake in fine droplets
- Fog cooling where a very fine fog is produced using a high pressure spray
- Special evaporative pads

Anti-Icing Systems

The formation of ice in the air intake or on the first few stages of the compressor can occur if a combination of temperature and humidity takes place (see Fig. 19). If chunks of ice are ingested into the compressor, major damage can result including catastrophic destruction of the compressor section blading.

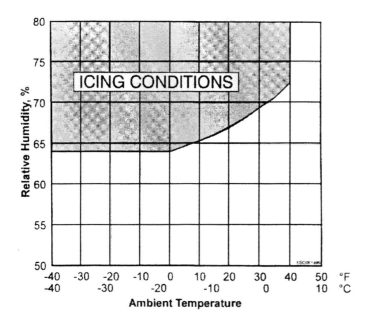

FIGURE 19

Range of Icing Conditions

Anti-icing systems may operate by:

- Bleeding air from the compressor and injecting it into the front of the compressor through the nose cone and the first few stator vanes (see Fig 20)

- Installing heating coils in the air intake

- Feeding heated air from some other source (such as the exhaust) into the air intake

Introducing warm air into the gas turbine intake will reduce the capacity of the unit, because warm air is less dense than cold air. The increase in air temperature means less mass will flow through the turbine. Because of this, anti-icing systems are activated only when icing conditions are present.

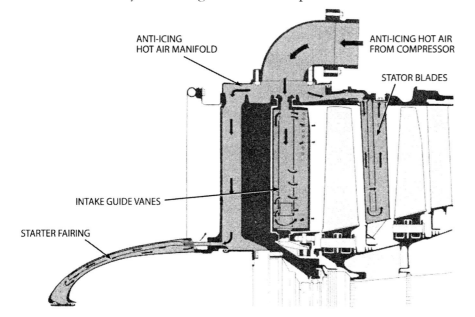

FIGURE 20

Anti-Icing System
(Courtesy of Rolls-Royce plc)

EXHAUST SYSTEM

The exhaust system directs the hot turbine exhaust, at the lowest possible pressure, to a location that is safe for employees and other equipment. It must be designed for the high temperature of the exhaust and be structurally sound. Noise attenuation and silencers may be required to meet local requirements. Care must be taken that the exhaust air does not re-circulate into the air intake since this will result in a loss of maximum power.

The exhaust may incorporate a heat exchange for regeneration or combined cycle installations. An example is shown in Fig. 21. Two gas turbines (GTA and GTB) exhaust into a common duct going to the water wall section of a boiler. The Heat Recovery Steam Generator (boiler) tubes are not shown, but they are connected to two steam drums. After leaving the boiler section, the exhaust gas provides heat to an economizer section, which preheats the boiler feedwater, and then travels to the stack and the atmosphere.

Immediately downstream of each of the turbine outlets, there is a diverter damper that permits the air to be exhausted directly to the atmosphere if the steam system is not operative. Prior to the heat recovery system, there is also a supplemental burner system to increase the exhaust temperature and thereby the recovery capacity of the boiler.

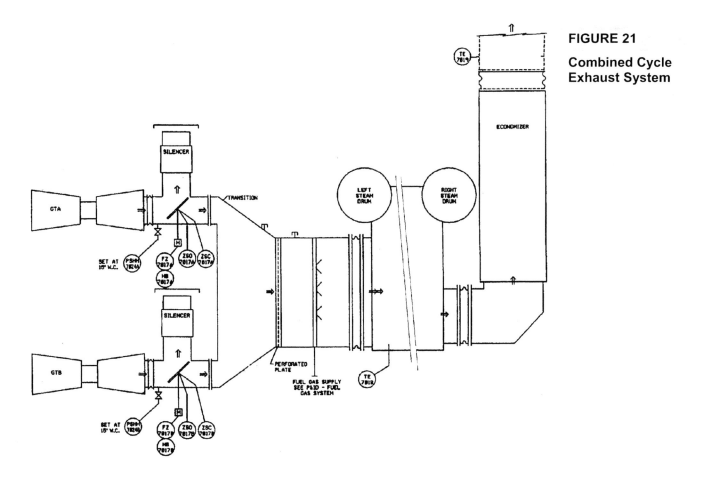

FIGURE 21

Combined Cycle Exhaust System

GAS TURBINE START-UP PROCEDURE

The basic steps in starting a gas turbine are:

- Preparation for startup
- Start initiation
- Crank and lightoff
- Warmup
- Loading.

These steps must occur in a specific sequence and at certain time intervals. They are usually managed by the control system and the operator often has no role except to watch the process. If certain conditions occur or specific requirements are not met at some point in the startup sequence, the startup will be aborted and the unit stopped. The progress of the startup is displayed on a control panel such as the one shown in Fig. 22.

FIGURE 22

**Typical Control Panel
Used to Monitor Startup,
Shutdown and
Operation**

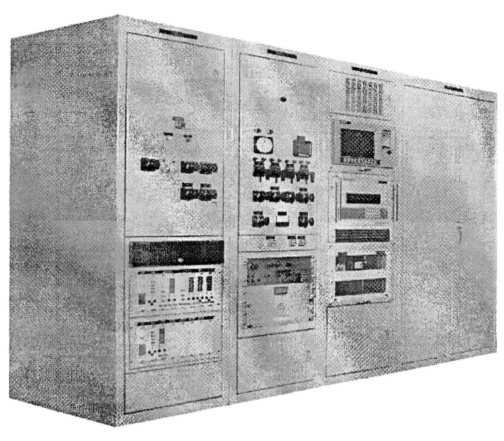

PREPARATION FOR STARTUP

When a start is initiated, it is assumed that all electrical, pneumatic, air, instrumentation and control systems are activated and energized. These systems will usually be active and will only need to be turned on if the equipment has been shut down for maintenance or an extended period of no demand. In remote applications, startup normally occurs automatically without human participation and intervention unless an abnormal situation requires response.

The operator may need to reset the system if a previous malfunction or abnormal condition has occurred. This is done by pressing a reset switch on the panel, or on a computer screen.

There are also a number of 'permissives' that need to be satisfied before the start sequence will be allowed by the control system. Some of these will pertain to the gas turbine, such as a minimum oil reservoir temperature, and others are related to the requirements of the particular load being driven by the turbine (typically an electrical generator or process/transmission gas compressor). Fig 23 shows an example of a startup screen for a gas turbine driving a gas compressor.

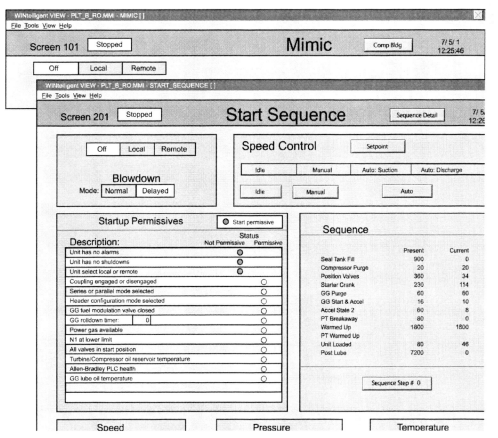

FIGURE 23

Startup Screen with Permissives
(Courtesy of Rolls-Royce plc)

Start Initiation

A gas turbine is normally in one of two modes of operation: remote or local. The mode of operation is set either by a switch on the control panel or a selection box on a computer screen. When in remote, a higher level process control system has the ability to initiate a start. When in local, the start can only be initiated from the control panel.

During the startup sequence, a number of operating conditions must be met as determined by various pressure, temperature and status switches. Timers are used to ensure these conditions occur in the expected time period, or else the startup will be aborted. An example of a startup sequence screen is given in Fig. 24. Notice the sequence of steps and the descriptions on the left of the screen.

FIGURE 24

Startup Screen with Sequencing Status
(Courtesy of Rolls-Royce plc)

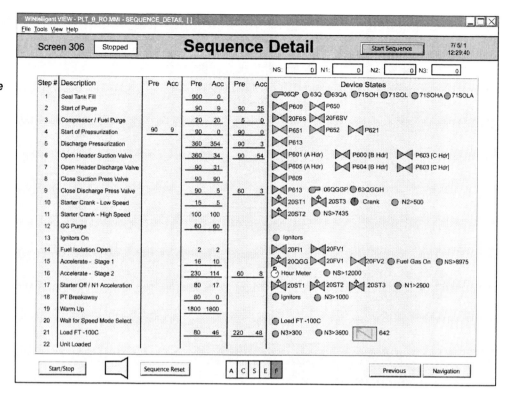

When the start button is pressed (locally or remotely), the following occurs:

- The ventilation fans starts – which vents the building or enclosure.

- Pre-lubrication occurs. Depending on the design of the lube oil system, the backup pump will start, and if adequate pressure is achieved within a certain time period, the pre-lube pump will start and the pre-lube timer resets to ensure adequate pressure.

- There may be a check of the fuel gas system to ensure that the fuel valves are operating properly and adequate fuel pressure is available.

Crank and Lightoff

Once these steps have been completed, the starter begins to rotate the gas turbine rotor (see Fig. 25). The first portion of this process purges the gas turbine for several minutes in case explosive vapors are still present. The rotor then coasts down to a speed appropriate for lightoff.

FIGURE 25

Startup of a Typical Gas Turbine

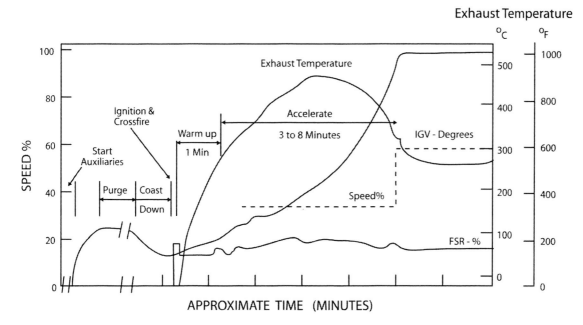

Fuel is then admitted to the combustion chambers, the igniters are energized and lightoff occurs. This results in a rapid increase in speed. The overrunning clutch disengages the starter, which then shuts down, and the igniters are de-energized.

Warmup

Once idle speed is reached, the engine is allowed to warm up. For backup power generation, especially for small gas turbines, this may be very short. When time is not as critical, it is best to permit the engine to warm up slowly. Heavy-duty gas turbines take longer to start and warm up than aero-derivatives.

On start initiation, the bleed valve(s) will be open and the inlet and variable guide vanes will be in their closed position. The bleed valves will close either at a certain speed or over a specified range of speeds. The guide vanes will open to their optimum position over a range of speeds as designated by a specified schedule (based on a control program that relates guide vane position to turbine speed).

Loading

After the warm-up is finished, the fuel flow is increased and the load is applied. For a generator, this will require synchronizing the speed, phase and voltage, and then closing the breaker.

If the gas turbine drives a compressor, the compressor will have been pressurized prior to the purge crank, and the suction and discharge valves will have been opened. The compressor is started in the unloaded position, with the recycle valve open. Loading is accomplished by slowly closing in on the recycle valve. The actual operating point will be determined by the control system.

The acceleration and deceleration of the gas turbine is limited to a certain rate. Sudden increases in speed will cause rapid increases in turbine temperature that could easily be above the limit. A rapid decrease in speed could cause combustion to be interrupted and any re-lighting, without going through the required start-up procedure, would be catastrophic.

NORMAL SHUTDOWN

Shutdown of a gas turbine is most often initiated by an operator although some systems do have an automatic shutdown when the gas turbine is no longer required. To a large extent, a shutdown is the reverse procedure of a startup.

The first step in a normal shutdown is to reduce speed to idle so the gas turbine can cool down. In this step the power turbine is unloaded, for example, by opening the breaker that connects the generator to the power system or opening the recycle valve of the compressor. The gas turbine cools down as much as possible to minimize the negative thermal effects. During this time, the engine can easily be restarted, according to the specified procedure.

When the cooldown timer times out, the fuel valve is closed which extinguishes combustion. The rotor speed decreases until the rotor stops.

As the speed drops, the main lube oil pump (if driven off the rotor) will lose pressure. At a specified point, usually based on oil pressure, the postlube pump starts up and continues to lubricate and cool the bearings for a specified time period.

The enclosure or building fans shut off.

On some gas turbines, the turning gear activates once the rotor stops.

FAST SHUTDOWN

In certain situations a fast shutdown will be initiated. This occurs when a protective device detects an abnormal condition such as high vibration, or when an operator initiates an emergency stop. In this case, the cooldown period is eliminated and the fuel valve is closed immediately. The rest of the shutdown sequence is the same as for a normal shutdown.

This type of shutdown increases the wear on the gas turbine because of the rapid cooldown it entails and is reserved for emergency conditions only.

ON-LINE AND OFF-LINE WATERWASH PROCEDURES

The major cause of deterioration in gas turbine performance is fouling of the compressor blading. Fouling results in a decrease in compressor efficiency which reduces overall thermal efficiency and maximum power. It will also result in compressor surging and acceleration problems.

The source of contamination is usually dust, salt and other airborne particles that are not trapped by the intake filters. Contamination can also come from other machinery close to the gas turbine or even the gas turbine exhaust being re-ingested under certain wind conditions. Sometimes, a compressor front bearing oil leak will make the problem worse.

Compressor cleaning can be accomplished by using either a liquid or an abrasive material. In the past, it was quite common for walnut shells or even rice (or other abrasive materials sometimes called carbo-blast) to be injected into the intake to abrasively clean the compressor blading. This is done while the unit is running and the materials are burnt up in the combustion section and then pass through the engine. Since it is not as effective as the waterwash method, it is not utilized as often any more. It also has the disadvantage of plugging up cooling passages in the compressor and cooling holes in the turbine blades.

The most effective method of compressor cleaning is the off-line waterwash. This method consists of stopping the unit, injecting waterwash fluids into the intake of the compressor while running on the starter and then restarting. It is also referred to as the crank-soak method.

On-line waterwashing is not as effective as off-line although it is still a viable alternative if downtime is not acceptable.

WATERWASH FLUIDS

The water that is used must be very clean and must conform to quality standards specified by the gas turbine vendor. Using hard water or water contaminated with sodium, potassium, vanadium or other chemicals can cause further fouling and increased corrosion.

To remove oily substances, additional cleaning agents and solvents need to be used. These are mixed with water and acceptable cleaners are often specified by gas turbine vendors. However, the most effective cleaning agents are also the most toxic and require special handling.

If the temperature is less than 40°F, a 1:1 mixture of water and ethylene glycol is recommended to prevent icing. Again the gas turbine vendor has to be consulted since commercial and automotive anti-freeze products are usually not acceptable.

Off-Line Waterwash

To perform an off-line waterwash, the engine is stopped and allowed to cool first. Some vendors specify that various instrumentation, bleed and drain lines be disconnected prior to water washing. The engine is then run at maximum crank speed with the fuel valve and igniters deactivated.

The waterwash fluid can be injected either through a pre-installed waterwash ring or provided manually by means of a hand-held sprayer. The waterwash ring can be installed on the intake bellmouth as shown in Fig. 26 or on the intake volute. As can be seen from Fig. 26, due to the difference in airflow, there are two ring assemblies depending whether an on-line or off-line wash is performed.

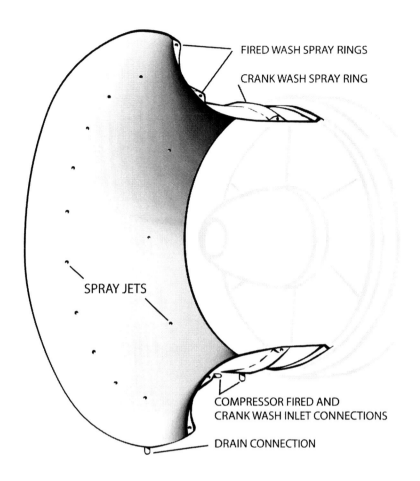

FIGURE 26

Waterwash Connections
(Courtesy of Rolls-Royce plc)

In some cases, operators will actually go into the intake to manually scrub and wash the first few stages with a brush if deposits are especially stubborn.

The waterwash fluids are contained in a special tank and the spray pressure is provided by compressed air applied to the tank. This tank may be permanently installed or located on a special cart such as the one shown in Fig. 27.

Once all of the fluids have been sprayed into the intake, all disconnected lines are reconnected and the unit restarted.

FIGURE 27

Waterwash Cart

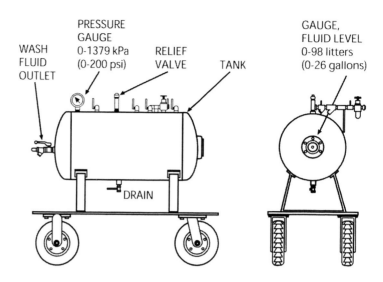

If the waterwash has been successful, the operator should be able to see an increase in compressor discharge pressure and a decrease in turbine inlet temperature.

On-Line Waterwash

To perform an on-line wash, the gas turbine is brought to idle and allowed to cool. The waterwash fluid or abrasive material is then injected after which the engine is returned to the required operating condition. This method is sometimes used to reduce the time between off-line washes.

UNIT 5

Introduction to Cogeneration

Here is what you will be able to do when you complete each objective:

1. Define Cogeneration

2. Describe two ways in which cogeneration can be achieved

3. Explain the flows through a typical cogeneration system

4. Explain the advantages of cogeneration

5. State some common users of cogeneration

6. Describe typical cogeneration installations using internal combustion engines and gas turbines

7. Describe control of a cogeneration system

INTRODUCTION

Industry, business and governments today are constantly concerned with two compelling needs, to operate efficiently and to operate with environmental responsibility. Both needs are significantly connected to the use, or misuse, of resources and energy.

Operating efficiently can mean the difference between success and failure of a company in today's competitive marketplace. An industry or business that uses or produces electrical or heat energy as part of its process must do so in the most economical ways possible. The costs of electricity and fuel are a significant operating expense and it is in the best economical interests to get the maximum value from both. This means that the electricity that is used in daily operations must be obtained at the least expensive rate and the fuel that is burned as part of a process must provide the greatest possible heat input to the process, with minimum heat losses.

Operating with environmental responsibility really means two things. First, there must be minimum consumption of the natural resources required by the process. Again this may refer to the use of fuels, such as natural gas, fuel oil, and even coal. Second, there must be a minimum of pollutants from the process into the environment. Minimizing air pollution is generally achieved by reducing the amount of fuels burned, by burning fuels as efficiently as possible, and by using the cleanest burning fuels available.

Industries and businesses that use substantial amounts of power and also require process heat in their operations are increasingly turning to a relatively new concept that permits them to generate both of these commodities themselves and thus operate with more efficiency and environmental responsibility than in the past. The method by which this is accomplished is called Cogeneration. Popular opinion suggests than Cogeneration may represent the future of power generation and building heating and may soon replace most existing small to medium-sized generation facilities.

What is Cogeneration ?

To understand cogeneration, it is necessary to know that most conventional power generation is based on burning a fuel in a boiler to produce steam. The pressure of this steam is then used to operate turbines that turn generators to produce electrical power. The sole purpose of burning the fuel is to produce electrical power.

A simplified version of this conventional method is shown in Figure 1.

FIGURE 1

Conventional Power
Production

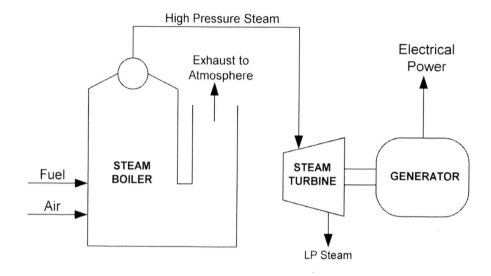

The conventional method is highly inefficient in that no more than one-third of the energy available in the original fuel can be converted into the steam pressure that generates electricity. The large majority of available energy in the fuel is lost in the exhaust from the steam boiler to atmosphere.

Cogeneration makes much better use of the fuel energy. In simple terms, it may be defined as the generation of two forms of energy from one process. Stated another way, it is a highly efficient means of simultaneously producing heat and power from a single energy source.

It can be achieved in two ways. The first way (Case 1) is to primarily burn a fuel to produce heat for a process (such as the incineration of waste) and then to use the waste heat from the process to produce steam in a boiler. Then use that steam in a steam turbine to turn a generator and produce electrical power. The second way (Case 2) is to primarily burn a fuel in a heat engine that turns a generator and produces electrical power. Then use the hot exhaust from the heat engine to produce steam or hot water for use in a process.

Figure 2 is a simplified sketch of Case 1 Cogeneration

FIGURE 2

Cogeneration using waste heat

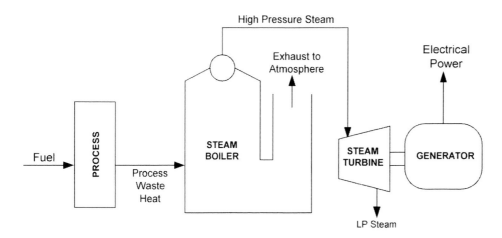

Figure 3 shows a simplified version of Case 2, which is the most common modern cogeneration arrangement and which the remainder of this module will describe. In terms of energy use and production it can be explained as follows:

- Fuel, usually natural gas or fuel oil, is burned in a heat engine and the energy produced by combustion is used to drive the engine. The engine, normally a gas turbine or internal combustion engine, is coupled to a power generator.

- Rotation of the engine is transferred to the power generator, which creates and delivers electrical energy in the form of AC power to a power distribution system. This power is used within the process or facility and any excess power is often sold to external customers.

- The hot exhaust gases from the heat engine are directed through a heat recovery generator (or boiler) that absorbs heat from the gases and converts water into either hotter water or steam. The latter are used for process purposes or building heat.

- Finally, the exhaust gases from the heat recovery generator are discharged to atmosphere. They contain much less wasted heat energy than if they had been exhausted directly from the heat engine.

FIGURE 3

Cogeneration, using a
heat engine

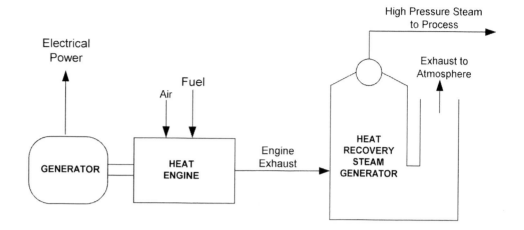

Advantages of Cogeneration

The increasing popularity of Cogeneration around the world suggests advantages
that are both local and global in nature. These include the following:

1. With the use of much cleaner burning fuels, cogeneration is reducing the
    load demand on heavier polluting, coal-fired generation facilities.

2. The demand for hydro-electric power generation has also been greatly
    reduced and in many areas future hydro-electric projects have been
    shelved in favor of cogeneration.

3. Businesses and industries that use substantial amounts of power can
    realize economic savings by producing, rather than purchasing, utilities.
    Economics are often further improved with the ability to sell excess
    power back to the utility companies.

4. The production of waste heat for process and heating purposes provides
    additional economic advantage.

5. Cogeneration plants can be configured to meet almost any industrial need
    and in a wide range of sizes, from a few hundred kilowatts to a few
    hundred megawatts. They can range from highly portable, skid-mounted
    systems to very large, permanent installations.

6. There is a much shorter start-up time for a cogeneration facility. Power can be available in minutes, compared to long warm-up times required of conventional plants. There is greater flexibility in the operations.

7. Cogeneration facilities are generally more compact and require less maintenance compared to a conventional plant of similar capacity.

Common Uses of Cogeneration

Cogeneration facilities can serve almost any industry or business that is energy intensive; ie. that consumes high amounts of electricity and/or requires high amounts of heat. The primary object generally is the production of electricity for internal use, with the availability of exhaust heat being a bonus that improves the economy of the installation. The list continues to grow, but typical users of cogeneration include:

Paper mills
Hospitals
Universities and colleges
Large public institutions (schools, hospitals, prisons)
Commercial laundries
Petrochemical, Refinery, and Gas Processing operations
Manufacturing operations
District heating and cooling plants

Typical Cogeneration Arrangements

As mentioned earlier, cogeneration facilties can exist in any number of configurations. Below are two of the more common types of installation, one using internal combustion engines and the other using gas turbines.

Figure 4 shows an arrangement that is very common in installations such as district or institution heating plants, where relatively small amounts of power are required (say in the 500-1500 kilowatt range) and the demand for heat is also relatively small. On the other hand, the total size of such a facility can be increased by simply adding more or larger engines and hot water generators.

In this arrangement, internal combustion engines, fueled by gas or light oil, are used to drive a number of generators. The hot exhaust from each engine discharges into a common header that carries it to a Heat Recovery Hot Water

Generator (HRHWG). Water in the facility's heating system is heated, circulated throughout the facility, then returned back to the HRHWG.

FIGURE 4

Typical Hot Water
Cogeneration System

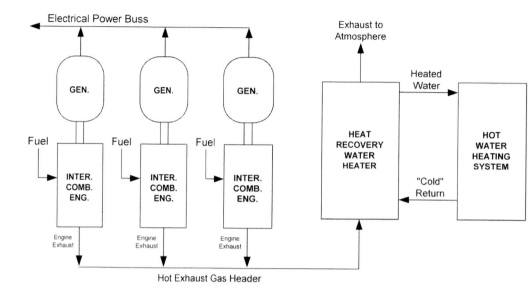

Figure 5 demonstrates a typical arrangement for a cogeneration facility using gas turbines.

Turbines are normally used when the power requirements are somewhat higher and there is a demand for high pressure steam. The gas turbine, which is an industrial version of an airplane jet engine, can be fueled with natural gas or fuel oil. Its design uses a compressor to draw in and compress large volumes of air, a combustor to burn the fuel and produce hot exhaust gases, and a turbine through which the gases expand to produce work and turn the generator. Since large volumes of hot exhaust gases are produced there is more heat available to the Heat Recovery Steam Generator (HRSG, often referred to as "hersig") so that relatively large volumes of high pressure steam can be produced. Typical production from a single gas turbine/hersig combination may be 1.5 – 60 megawattts.

While the arrangement in Fig. 5 shows two gas turbines exhausting through a single HRSG, it is more usual in larger installations to have a dedicated HRSG for each turbine.

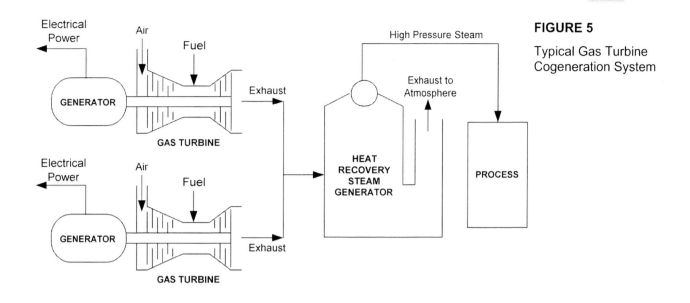

FIGURE 5

Typical Gas Turbine Cogeneration System

Control of a Cogeneration System

In this type of cogeneration system there are two main factors that must be controlled. These are the power production and the steam production. There is a demand for both of these products at any given time, dictated by the process requirements for heat and power or by the external demand if excess power is being sold outside the facility.

Power production control is relatively simple. If the external system demands more power from the generator then the fuel supply to the gas turbine (or engine) increases, allowing the turbine to do more work and thus maintain the generator speed at the increased load. Conversely, if the system demands less power then the fuel to the turbine decreases, reducing the work output of the turbine.

Steam (or hot water) production is a bit more complicated. The exhaust gases from the gas turbine (or engine) are about proportional to the power generation. That is, if power production increases, the turbine will burn more fuel and there will be more exhaust gases available to the HRSG. Likewise, if power production drops off there will be less hot gases available to the HRSG. However, if the steam demand from the process does not also change in synch with the power production then the HRSG will receive either too much or too little exhaust heat to satisfy the steam demand. Steam production must therefore be controlled by adjusting the amount of heat that is delivered to the HRSG.

Figure 6 illustrates how this is normally accomplished.

FIGURE 6

Cogeneration Control
with Duct Burners and
Diverter Valve

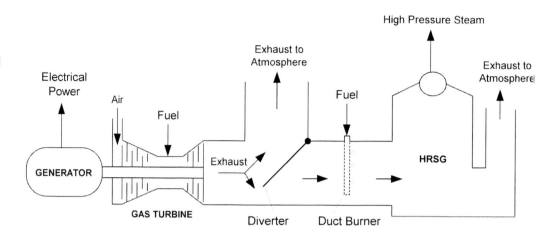

A set of Duct Burners are located between the turbine (or engine) exhaust and the HRSG. If the turbine is delivering insufficient exhaust gases to satisfy the steam demand then the duct burners will fire to produce the extra heat required. If the turbine is providing enough exhaust heat then the duct burners would be off. Also, if the turbine is exhausting more heat than the HRSG requires, then this heat must be diverted away from the HRSG. This is done through a Diverter Valve (damper) that sends a controlled amount of exhaust gases directly to atmosphere. The overall control scheme for this system operates the duct burners and the diverter valve(s) together so that a constant steam pressure is maintained from the HRSG.

UNIT 6

Cogeneration Systems and Operations

Learning Objectives

Here is what you will be able to do when you complete each objective:

1. Define cogeneration and explain its purpose, advantages, and applications.

2. Explain the components and operation of simple-cycle cogeneration systems.

3. Explain the components and operation of combined-cycle, gas/steam turbine cogeneration systems.

4. Explain the components and operation of a fully fired, combined-cycle cogeneration system.

5. Explain single-shaft and dual-shaft combined-cycle power plants.

6. Explain the control strategies and components, for both power and steam production, including diverter and duct burner operation.

7. Describe the various designs of heat recovery steam generators (HRSGs) and explain their industrial applications.

8. Explain the environmental considerations and techniques in the operation of a cogeneration system.

9. Describe typical cogeneration systems that use internal combustion engines (gas or diesel) and heat recovery water heaters (HRWHs).

10. Explain a typical start-up procedure for a combined cycle cogeneration system.

COGENERATION

Cogeneration can be defined as the utilization of one form of input energy to generate two (or more) forms of output energy. The input energy may be natural gas, gasoline, diesel, oil or coal, or a variety of waste fuels from industrial processes. The primary type of energy output may be mechanical energy, which can be used for:

- Driving an alternator for electrical production
- Driving rotating equipment, such as motors, fans, pumps and compressors

The secondary type of energy output utilizes the heat energy that is normally lost. This thermal energy is used for direct process applications or for the production of steam, hot water, or chilled water (absorption refrigeration).

Most modern installations will have a gas turbine, gas engine or diesel engine generating electricity. The waste heat will be used to produce steam or hot water in some form of heat recovery boiler.

Purpose

The primary purpose of cogeneration is to reduce energy costs. A traditional plant using boilers, gas turbines, or internal combustion engines has an overall efficiency less than 40%. Cogeneration can increase the plant overall energy efficiency to a value between 60% and 90%.

Advantages

There are several advantages of cogeneration at both the micro (local) and macro (global) levels which have resulted in an increasing popularity of cogeneration units for business and industry.

1. Micro (Local) Level

Advantages at the micro (local) level include:

- A reduction in the total energy bill when electricity and heat are required at the site. Economics may be further improved with the ability to sell excess power back to the utility companies.

- Cogeneration facilities are generally more compact and require less maintenance compared to a conventional plant of similar capacity.

- A cogeneration facility has a much shorter start-up time than a conventional plant of similar capacity.

- A wide range of configurations and sizes to meet the requirements of almost any industrial facility.

2. Macro (Global) Level

Advantages at the macro (global) level include:

- Cogeneration facilities that utilize cleaner burning fuels will reduce the load demand on heavier polluting, coal-fired generation facilities.

- The greater efficiency of cogeneration facilities will result in less fuel being burned resulting in preservation of energy reserves and the subsequent reduction in the emission of green house gases (especially CO_2)

- Electrical production on site will reduce the requirement for the construction of new, large and expensive utility plants. Local production of electricity also results in a reduction of transmission line losses.

Applications

Cogeneration facilities are serving a growing list of business and industry facilities. The applications of cogeneration can fall into three general areas.

- Schools, hospitals, hotels, universities, colleges, prisons, malls and other institutional or commercial establishments that have a heating and electrical demand for twenty four hours a day. The heating requirements of these facilities can normally be met with a fairly low temperature heat recovery unit.

- Pulp and paper mills, petrochemical plants, refineries, gas processing plants, food processing plants and other large scale industrial processes. These types of plants may require high temperature energy for some processes or require low temperature from refrigeration units, or both.

- Localized central heating and cooling plants situated in industrial areas or city centers, supplying the electrical, heating and cooling requirements for a number of buildings or small industrial plants.

SIMPLE CYCLE COGENERATION SYSTEMS

There are various types of simple-cycle cogeneration systems being used today. They include the following:

- Back Pressure Steam Turbine
- Waste Heat Cogeneration
- Heat Engine Cogeneration
- Gas Turbine

Back Pressure Steam Turbine

The backpressure steam turbine, as shown in Fig. 1, is a type of a simple-cycle cogeneration system. The system shown consists of a fuel, which may be gas, oil, coal, or waste fuel, burned in a boiler. The steam produced drives a steam turbine, which in turn supplies mechanical energy to an alternator. The LP (Low Pressure) exhaust steam from the turbine is controlled at a specific pressure to supply the required heat to the process. The condensed steam from the process is returned to the boiler.

FIGURE 1

Back Pressure Steam Turbine Cogeneration

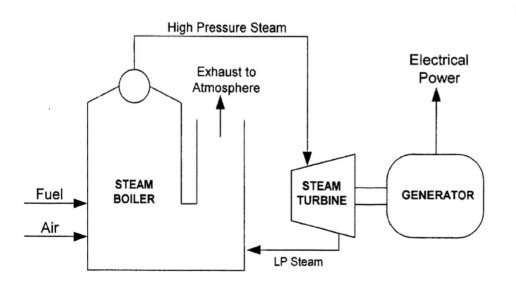

Waste Heat Cogeneration

Fig. 2 shows a simple sketch of a waste heat cogeneration system. The primary purpose is to burn a fuel to produce heat for a process and then to use the waste heat from the process to produce steam in the boiler. The steam from the boiler is fed to the steam turbine to turn a generator and produce electrical power. The LP (Low Pressure) exhaust steam from the turbine is used to drive other turbines or in feedwater heaters. The process may be the incineration of municipal waste or wood wastes from a pulp mill.

FIGURE 2

**Waste Heat
Cogeneration**

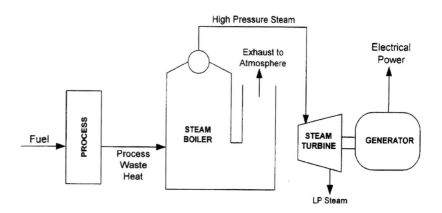

Heat Engine Cogeneration

Fig. 3 is a simple sketch of a heat engine cogeneration system. The fuel used may be natural gas, oil, gasoline, or diesel. The heat engine turns a generator for the production of electricity and the exhaust gases from the heat engine provide the heat source for the heat recovery unit. The steam produced may be utilized for building heating or an industrial process.

FIGURE 3

**Heat Engine
Cogeneration**

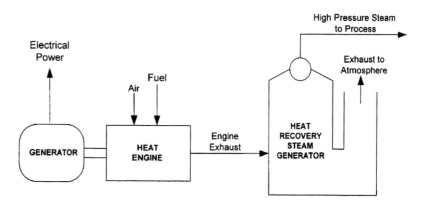

Gas Turbines

Fig. 4 is a simple line sketch of a gas turbine turning an electrical generator. The waste heat, produced by the gas turbine, passes through an exhaust heat boiler. The steam produced by the boiler is used for heating purposes and for an absorption refrigeration system. This unit may be used to provide heating and cooling for an office building, shopping center, or public institution.

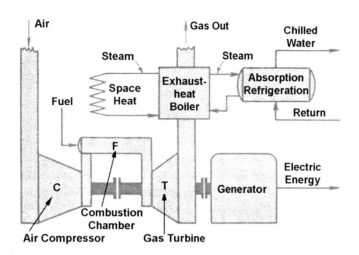

FIGURE 4

Waste Heat Cogeneration

COMBINED-CYCLE SYSTEMS

Combined cycle cogeneration refers to the production of electricity from two sources utilizing one fuel source. The combined cycle cogeneration system, shown in Fig. 5, has a gas turbine and its compressor. Fuel, for the gas turbine, is burned in the conventional gas turbine combustors. The exhaust from the gas turbine is used as the combustion air for the boiler, which produces steam for the condensing steam turbine. This steam not only drives the steam turbine, but it is bled off from sections of the turbine and used as a heat source in the feed heaters. The steam turbine is connected to a second electrical generator.

Since the boiler is "pressurized" by the gas turbine exhaust, neither forced draft (FD) nor induced draft (ID) fans are required. The combustion of fuel in the boiler is an entirely separate process and does not affect the gas turbine so that any boiler fuel may be used in this case.

FIGURE 5

Combined-Cycle Gas/Steam Turbine Cogeneration System

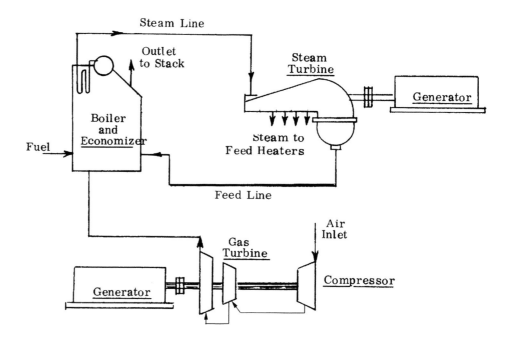

The combined cycle unit, shown in Fig. 6, demonstrates a different configuration. The compressor supplies pressurized combustion air to the boiler, with the outlet gases from the boiler being fed to the gas turbine. The products of combustion in the boiler are used as the working gas for the gas turbine so that, in this case, the fuel used in the boiler must be acceptable for the gas turbine, particularly with regard to blade fouling.

The hot exhaust gases from the gas turbine heat the incoming feedwater in the economizer. The gas turbine is coupled to an electrical generator and the steam, produced in the boiler, drives a steam turbine. This steam turbine, in turn, runs a second electrical generator.

FIGURE 6

Combined-Cycle Steam/Gas Turbine Cogeneration System

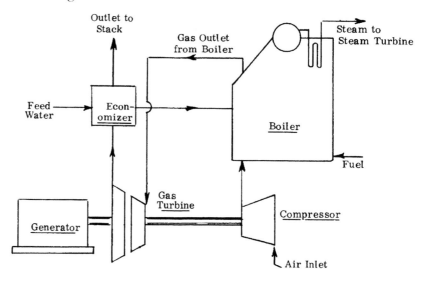

The combined cycle shown in Fig. 7 shows a generator on the same shaft as the compressor/turbine. The exhaust gases from the gas turbine pass into the heat recovery steam generator (HRSG) where superheated steam is produced. The superheated steam passes to a steam turbine connected to another generator, and the exhaust steam is condensed and returned to the boiler.

FIGURE 7

Combined Cycle System Schematic
(Courtesy of Babcock and Wilcox)

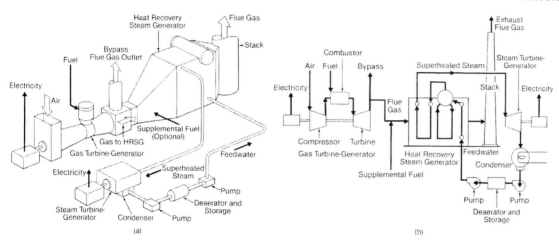

FULLY FIRED COMBINED-CYCLE COGENERATION SYSTEM

A fully fired combined-cycle cogeneration system is shown in Fig. 8. This system consists of a gas turbine, steam turbine, generators and a fired heat recovery steam generator (HRSG). The gas and steam turbines are each coupled to a generator.

Ambient air is drawn through the inlet air system where it is filtered and directed to the inlet of the air compressor section of the gas turbine. The air is compressed and passed to the combustion chamber where it is mixed with fuel, natural gas or oil, and is then ignited. The compressed and heated combustion gases flow to the turbine section where these hot gases expand. The expansion of these gases creates work, which drives the compressor and an electricity generator.

The hot gases, leaving the gas turbine, still contains energy, which would be wasted if the gas turbine were used alone or in "open cycle" mode. In a combined cycle plant, the heat recovery steam generator (HRSG) extracts most of this remaining energy to produce steam. But, the absorption of this heat energy in the HRSG is not sufficient to maintain the designed volume and/or temperature of the steam entering the steam turbine. Therefore, the heat recovery steam generator (HRSG) also contains a series of auxiliary burners, which are used to maintain these steam conditions. These auxiliary burners also use natural gas, or oil, as fuel.

The steam, produced in the HRSG unit, is used to drive a turbine that is connected to a generator. The steam, after expanding in the steam turbine, enters the condenser where it is condensed into water through the use of circulating cooling water. This condensate, or water, is then pumped to the HRSG unit.

The extra electricity produced by the "combined cycle" plant results in a significant increase in thermal efficiency. This means less fuel is used and emissions to atmosphere are lower when compared to a conventional, steam generating plant.

FIGURE 8

Fully Fired Combined-Cycle Cogeneration System

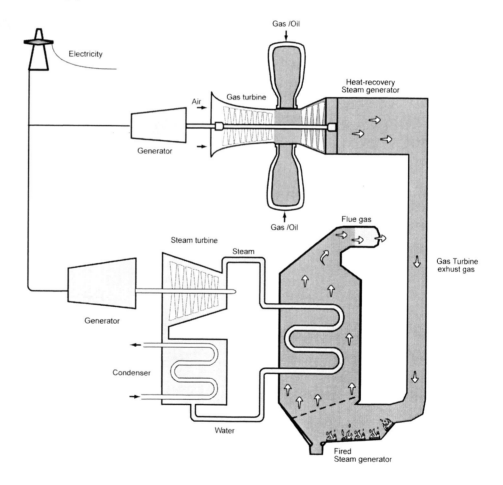

SINGLE-SHAFT COMBINED-CYCLE POWER PLANT

A single shaft combined-cycle power plant has the compressor, gas turbine and generator all on a common shaft. This arrangement, shown in Fig. 9, has the generator in between the gas turbine and the steam turbine. In this manner, the energy output of the gas and steam turbines are applied to a common generator.

Countries with small capacity systems, may require small capacity additions, favor combined cycle power plants in the range of 134 million to 400 million hp. This can be easily accommodated with a large gas turbine and a steam turbine located on a single shaft.

The most attractive operating and performance characteristics of any power plant arrangements are achieved in a combined cycle with a single-shaft gas/steam turbine arrangement. Such power blocks provide the following major benefits:

- Highest level of thermal efficiency
- Extremely low capital costs
- Highest operating flexibility, for example, fast start-up
- Short project and construction times
- Low operation and maintenance costs

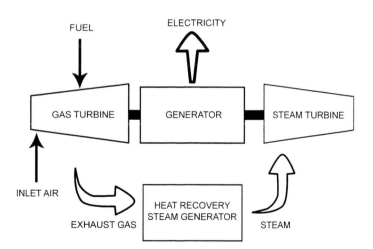

FIGURE 9

Single Shaft Combined-Cycle Power Plant

Fi. 10 is another type of single shaft arrangement in which the gas turbine is attached to the generator. The hot exhaust gas from the gas turbine pass to the heat recovery steam generator where steam is produced and used in process work.

FIGURE 10

Single Shaft Combined-Cycle Power Plant

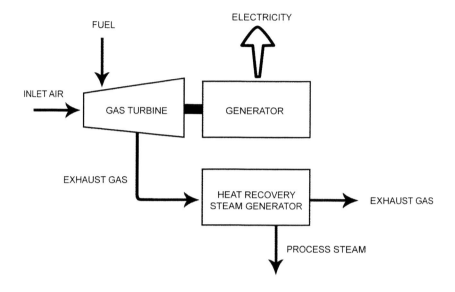

Fig. 11 is a diagram of the actual layout of a single shaft combined cycle power plant.

FIGURE 11

Single Shaft Combined-Cycle Power Plant

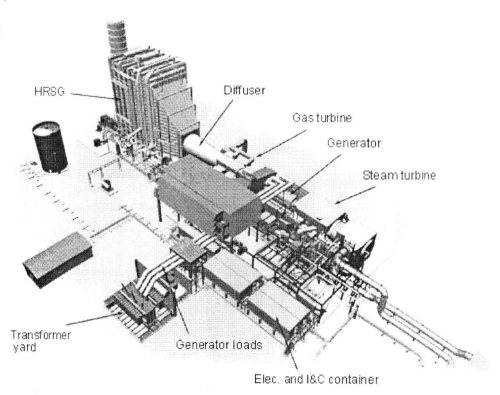

DUAL-SHAFT COMBINED-CYCLE POWER PLANT

A dual shaft combined-cycle power plant arrangement, shown in Fig. 12, consists of one gas turbine and one steam turbine. The exhaust gases from the gas turbine are routed to the heat-recovery steam generator, to raise superheated steam for the turbine without any additional fuel consumption. A generator is attached to the steam turbine and the gas turbine for the generation of power.

Countries with smaller grids or special grid requirements prefer multi-shaft combined cycle plants with several smaller gas turbines in the same power range combined with one or more steam turbines. Multi-shaft type has high efficiency at base load operation.

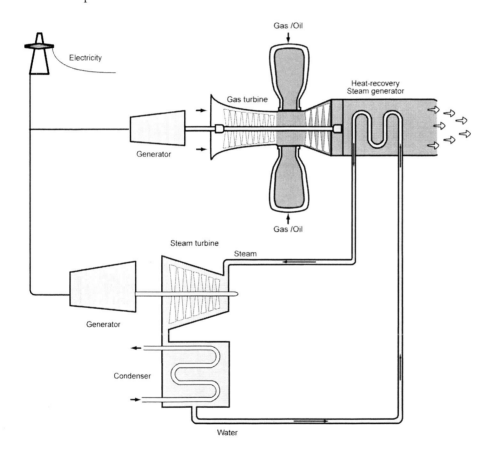

FIGURE 12

Dual Shaft Combined-Cycle Cogeneration System

CONTROL STRATEGIES

The selection of a control strategy will be dependant on the primary function of the cogeneration system as determined by the type of facility. The fuel supplied may first produce electrical power with the thermal energy produced as a byproduct. This type of cogeneration system, called a topping cycle cogeneration, may be used in institutional or commercial establishments such as hospitals, colleges, universities, pulp and paper, and food processing. In a bottoming cycle cogeneration system, the primary fuel produces high temperature thermal energy for processes such as steel making, gas plants, and petrochemical facilities. The heat exhausted from these processes is utilized to produce electrical energy from a HRSG.

Electrical Load Control

The cogeneration system may be connected to the utility grid or be separated from the electrical utility grid. A system that is not connected to the electrical grid will supply all of the electrical requirements of the site, including that required for emergency backup and shutdowns. The process utilizes the waste heat from the electrical production. Some waste heat may be lost to the atmosphere if the heating requirements of the process are less than the heat produced by the system. Other heating systems, such as boilers or auxiliary firing, may be required if the waste heat produced is less than that required for the process.

A system connected to the electrical grid may be either a base loaded system or a set electrical demand from the utility grid. The base loaded system has the electrical production from the cogeneration system fixed at its maximum production and changing electrical requirements met by the electrical utility grid. The set electrical demand has the electrical supply from the utility grid fixed and the cogeneration system looks after the changing electrical requirements. In both cases, the sizing of the system may require the ability to exhaust excess waste heat or to supply additional heat to the process from other boilers or from auxiliary firing.

Thermal Load Control

The thermal load control may be either a fixed production of a minimum thermal energy or varying requirement for thermal energy. With the first strategy, the production of the thermal energy is fixed at the minimum requirements for the site, and the prime mover will operate at full load, all the time. Further thermal requirements are met using other boilers or auxiliary firing. The second strategy involves the production of thermal energy to meet the changing requirements of the process at all times. In this case, the prime mover will have a varying output. Either purchasing or selling power to the electrical utility grid meets changes in electrical requirements for both of these strategies.

Diverter and Duct Burner Control

Fig. 13 shows a control system utilizing a duct burner and a diverter. Low thermal requirement may occur during startup, during times of low production for a process, or low electrical requirements in the case of a combined cycle. During low thermal requirements, the diverter valve is positioned to close off the exhaust gases to the HRSG. These exhaust gases are then vented to the atmosphere. As the thermal requirements increase, the diverter is positioned to allow more and more exhaust gases through the HRSG. Once the diverter is positioned to completely close off the exhaust gases to the atmosphere, the duct burner (auxiliary firing) will begin to fire and modulate to control further changes in the requirements for thermal energy.

FIGURE 13

Cogeneration Control with Duct Burners and Diverter Valve

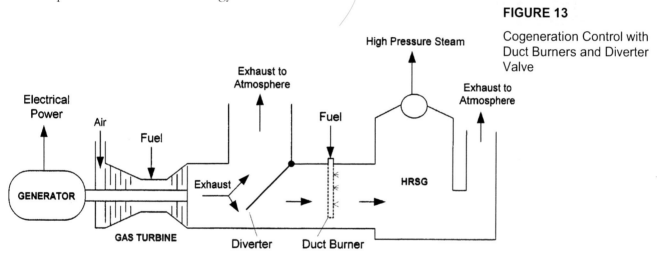

HEAT RECOVERY STEAM GENERATOR (HRSG)

The heat recovery steam generator (HRSG) is sometimes referred to as a waste heat recovery boiler (WHRB), or turbine exhaust gas (TEG) boiler. The main application for these boilers is steam generation using gas turbine exhaust gas as a heat source.

The specific design of the HRSG will be dependant on the electrical requirements of the plant (gas turbine size) and the thermal requirements of the plant site. The flexibility of the HRSG allows for different industrial configurations to meet the specific requirements of each specific plant site.

The gas flow can be either horizontal or vertical, depending upon the floor space available. The horizontal type is the most common. The HRSG may be designed for operation with multiple separate pressure steam-water loops to meet applications requirements and maximize heat recovery. Circulation of HRSG may be forced circulation or natural circulation with most horizontal gas flow HRSG boilers using natural circulation. Some HRSG boilers are of the once through forced circulation design. Some have high alloy tubes, and can operate without water-flow through the tubes.

FIGURE 14

HRSG with Auxiliary Firing

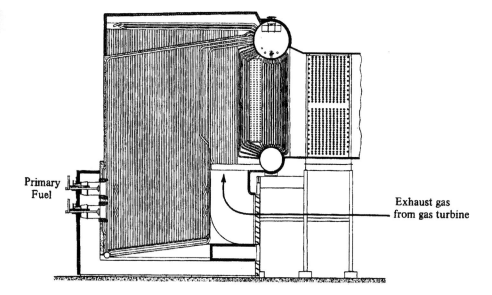

HRSG units may be unfired (waste heat only) or have auxiliary, or duct, burners to raise the gas temperature inlet of the HRSG coils. The duct burners can be used to:

- Increase the production of steam
- Control the superheater temperatures
- Meet process steam temperature requirements

The HRSG, as shown in Fig.14, has a duct burner. Heating surfaces include: superheater, boiler/evaporator tubes, and an economizer. It is a natural circulation boiler with a steam drum. This HRSG would be found at a plant site with a fairly high electrical requirement (larger gas turbine) and a requirement for superheated steam, possibly for steam turbines in a combined cycle cogeneration plant.

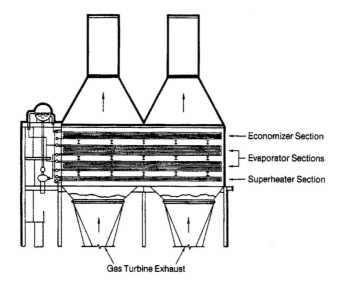

FIGURE 15

Vertical HRSG
(Courtesy of Combustion Engineering)

The vertical HRSG in Fig. 15 has two ducts for gas turbine exhaust. It is a drum type with natural circulation. The horizontal HRSG as shown in Fig. 16, is used in a cogeneration cycle. It produces high-pressure steam at 1,000 psi, which is fed to a turbine generator. It has an intermediate (350 psi) and a low-pressure (50 psi) steam drum. The steam from these drums is used for process heating.

FIGURE 16

External view of Horizontal HRSG
(Courtesy of Babcock and Wilcox)

ENVIRONMENTAL CONCERNS

The environmental impact of a cogeneration system will be dependant on the type of fuel used and the type of prime mover, either gas turbine or internal combustion engine. Cogeneration systems can be designed for coal, oil, gasoline, natural gas, and waste fuels.

Each of these fuels has their own environmental impact, due to the formation of the following gases:

- Nitrous oxides
- Carbon dioxide
- Sulphur dioxide

Nitrous Oxides (NO$_X$)

Oxides of nitrogen (NO$_X$) are produced by burning a fuel in air. The level of NO$_X$ emissions is dependent on combustion conditions and particularly on temperature, pressure, combustion chamber geometry and the air/fuel mixture.

The primary environmental consideration for natural gas is the development of nitrous oxides (NO$_X$) due to the high temperature of combustion. The production of nitrous oxides leads to acid rain and are generally regulated by local environmental agencies. The newer combustor designs have greatly reduced the development of NO$_X$ within the gas turbine. In locations where there is a greater environmental requirement for the reduction of nitrous oxides, the temperature of the flame can be reduced by the injection of steam into the combustion region, thereby greatly reducing the development of nitrous oxides. But, this has the disadvantage of reducing the temperature of the exhaust gases through the HRSG and therefore, reducing the efficiency of the unit.

The formation of nitrous oxides can also be reduced through the use of selective catalytic reduction (SCR). This involves the injection of ammonia prior to the catalyst. This process is extremely dependant on temperature and the flexibility of the HRSG allows the ammonia and catalyst to be installed at a precise location in the temperature profile of the exhaust gases exiting the gas turbine. The exhaust gases leaving the gas turbine are about 1020°F and the optimal temperature for SCR is between 660°F and 850°F. The use of SCR with steam injection can reduce the nitrous oxides from 150 ppm to less than 10 ppm. Fig. 17 shows the ammonia injection and SCR in a HRSG.

FIGURE 17

Selective Catalytic Reduction of NO$_X$
(Courtesy of Babcock and Wilcox)

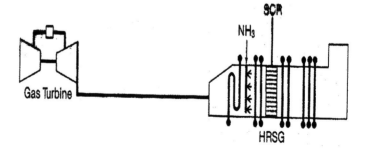

Carbon Dioxide

The most important product of the combustion process is carbon dioxide, well known for its contribution to the greenhouse effect and climatic change. However, where cogeneration replaces the separate fossil fuel generation of electricity and heat, it reduces primary fuel consumption by about 35%. This means a similar reduction in CO_2 emissions.

Sulphur Dioxide

Emissions of sulphur dioxide vary directly with the sulphur content of the fuel. In the case of natural gas, this is negligible and condensing heat exchangers can be used to maximize heat recovery wherever appropriate. Diesel fuel and biogas do contain sulphur and where the sulphur content exceeds the limit set by the manufacturer, some form of fuel cleaning is necessary prior to use. Furthermore, the cost of installing a stainless steel heat exchanger and exhaust flue to counter the corrosive nature of the condensate usually precludes the use of condensing heat recovery systems with these fuels.

INTERNAL COMBUSTION ENGINE COGENERATION SYSTEMS

For small facilities an internal combustion (IC) engine with an electrical generator and heat recovery water heater (HRWH) may provide sufficient electrical and thermal energy to meet requirements. The IC engine may be burning diesel, propane, natural gas or gasoline, depending on the local availability and cost. In small systems, the IC engine with a HRWH can be quite efficient, especially if the system is designed with water jackets to:

- Recover the heat produced to cool the engine
- Cool the air surrounding the engine
- Cool the lubricating oil of the engine

The IC engine has the added advantage of being capable of intermittent operation when required, and not being subjected to load changes due to changes in ambient temperature (as a gas turbine would be). Fig. 18 shows an internal combustion engine turning a generator (not shown) with the exhaust gases either passing to atmosphere or through a HRWH. The water flow is from the process to the oil cooler, then to the air cooler, and finally to the water cooler before passing to the hot water (or steam) coils. The heat recovery water heater may be of the completely filled boiler (non evaporator) or of the once through tubular design.

This type of installation would be used where the electrical energy demand is higher than the thermal energy demand. Small businesses and institutions may find this type of system functional for providing all or part of the electrical and thermal requirements.

FIGURE 18

**Cogeneration Using
Internal Combustion
Engine**

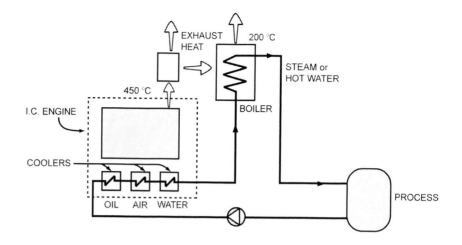

HEAT RECOVERY WATER HEATER

Fig. 19 shows an arrangement that is very common in installations such as district or institution heating plants, where relatively small amounts of power are required (670 to 2,000 hp) and the demand for heat is also relatively small. In this arrangement, internal combustion engines fueled by gas or light oil are used to drive a number of generators. The hot exhaust from each engine discharges into a common header that carries it to a Heat Recovery Hot Water Generator (HRHWG). Water in the facility's heating system is heated and then circulated throughout the facility and returned back to the HRHWG.

FIGURE 19

Hot Water Cogeneration
System

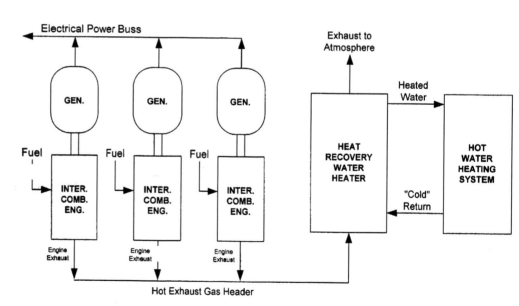

GENERAL START-UP PROCEDURE

The start up sequence of each cogeneration system will be unique to the specific design of the installation. The manufacturers guidelines and operating instructions should be consulted prior to attempting to start the system. The start up sequence may be as easy as pushing a button and having electronic controls proceed through the start sequence or as complex as a major power plant start up. The start up sequence found below would be for a small (under 5 MW) electrical generation plant with the waste heat supplying a steam turbine attached to a generator, or supplying heat to a absorption refrigeration system, or supplying the heating system directly.

With reference to Fig. 20 and Fig. 21, the following is a brief overview of the starting sequence of this system.

1) The operator initiates a turbine start up from the control room. A programmable logic controller (PLC) directs the starter motor through the start up and speed commands.

2) The PLC sends the following commands to the variable frequency driver (VFD).
   a) EY9016A   -   Close Starter Motor A Breaker
   b) EY9016B   -   Close Starter Motor B Breaker
   c) SC9015 A   -   Gas Turbine "A" Starter Motor Speed Control
   d) SC9015 B   -   Gas Turbine "B" Starter Motor Speed Control

3) The PLC receives the following information from the starter system
   a) ZSC9002A   -   Gas Turbine "A" Starter Breaker Closed
   b) ZSC9002B   -   Gas Turbine "B" Starter Breaker Closed

4) The turbine is rotated to about 55% of rated speed using a 480 V variable frequency drive electric motor. A clutch in the gearbox will keep the starter motor engaged until the torque from the driver is overcome by the torque of the turbine.

5) During start up, the diverter valve will be open to atmosphere and the air from the turbine will pass up through the silencer, purging the gas turbine of combustibles. At 25% rated speed, the diverter valve will reposition to allow air to pass through the HRSG, purging any combustible gases from this region. The diverter valve is again repositioned to pass the exhaust gases to atmosphere through the silencer.

6) The turbine is then run up to staring speed (55% of rated speed) and the fuel is admitted to the combustor and ignited. The generator is then allowed to pick up electrical load.

7) Once the generator is stable, the diverter valve is slowing opened to allow hot combustion gases to enter the HRSG and slowly warm the water in the tubes. Once the HRSG is producing steam, the diverter valve is opened to allow 100% of the combustion gases to pass through the HRSG. The auxiliary burner may be started once the diverter is closed and steam demand is high enough to require the additional firing.

8) The steam turbine is started and its generator is allowed to pick up the additional electrical load, following the manufacturers recommended startup procedure.

FIGURE 20

Gas Turbine Starter Schematic

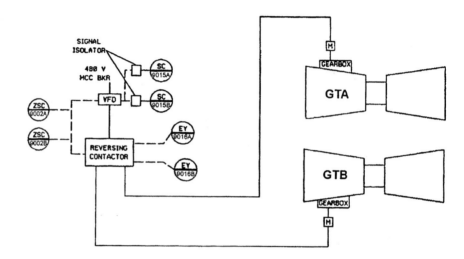

FIGURE 21

Gas Turbine Exhaust
Schematic

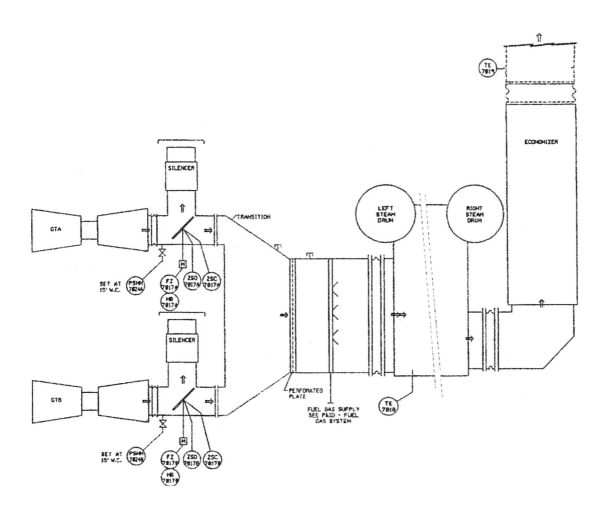

UNIT 7

Lubrication and Bearings

Here is what you will be able to do when you complete each objective:

1. Explain the purposes of lubrication

2. Describe the classes of lubricants and their appropriate uses

3. Describe the properties of lubricating oils

4. Explain the purposes of oil additives

5. Explain boundary and fluid film lubrication as it applies to bearings

6. Describe shell or sleeve bearings and explain their lubrication methods

7. Describe ball and roller bearing designs and applications and explain their lubrication

8. Explain symptoms of and reasons for bearing failure

9. Sketch and describe a typical forced-feed lube oil skid

10. Sketch and describe a simple lube oil system for a gas turbine

INTRODUCTION

The problem of friction between two surfaces, such as the shaft and a bearing surfaces on a motor, pump, or other rotating machinery, can be partially overcome through the use of proper lubrication. This reduction of friction has a considerable effect on energy savings, smoothness of machine operation, and temperature control of the two surfaces involved. Proper and diligent lubrication prevents equipment damage and reduces maintenance costs and downtime.

Since there are many types of bearing arrangements, each having its own operating characteristics, it is necessary to provide lubricants that match the operating principles of the bearings and the operating conditions of temperature, humidity, speed, etc.

Equipment manufacturers supply very specific guidelines and procedures for the lubrication, care and maintenance of the rotating parts of equipment and the onus is on the operators to ensure these are followed faithfully. The information in this module is of a general nature only, so that the operator will have the basic knowledge to understand manufacturers' instructions.

LUBRICATION PRINCIPLES

Friction between two surfaces can be defined quite simply as resistance to motion (or attempted motion). Suppose, for example, that two flat pieces of metal rest upon each other as in Fig. 1. It might appear that smoothly-ground surfaces such as these would offer little or no resistance to the movement of one over the other. When these surfaces are viewed under a microscope, however, they are found to be made up of innumerable irregularities similar to the hills and valleys. The interlocking of these irregularities produces a definite resistance to motion.

FIGURE 1

Surface Lubrication

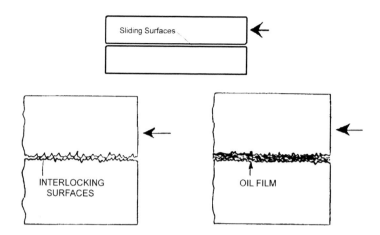

Lubrication involves the separation of surfaces that are moving in relation to each other and that would otherwise be in contact with each other. The separation of these surfaces is achieved by interposing a substance between them. This substance, known as a **lubricant**, has other functions besides the separation of surfaces.

LUBRICANT PURPOSES

There are several reasons for using lubricants. The most important are reduction of friction and wear, but others include corrosion control, shock absorption, sealing, and temperature control.

Friction Reduction

As shown in Fig. 1, even finely machined surfaces are not completely smooth and, if viewed under a microscope, the surfaces can be seen to consist of hills and valleys. When two surfaces rub together, their hills and valleys interlock and extra force is required to move the surfaces across each other. Also, where the materials contact each other, they tend to cling or weld together and this compounds the extra force required for motion. The extra force required is known as the force of friction and it can be considerably reduced by using a lubricant to separate the two moving surfaces.

Wear Reduction

When two surfaces are rubbing together, the high spots or hills will break away (wear) due to striking against each other. In some circumstances this will result in the surfaces becoming smoother, in which case the wear is beneficial. However, often the wearing process causes large pieces of material to be torn away and this results in even rougher surfaces and therefore increased friction and wearing.

If the surfaces can be separated from each other by a lubricant so that their high spots do not come in contact with each other, then the wear will be reduced or eliminated.

Corrosion Reduction

Besides separating the bearing surfaces, the lubricant forms a film on the surfaces, thus protecting them from corrosion. The film isolates the surfaces from contact with oxygen or other contaminating gases or fluids. Often chemical compounds (additives) are purposely added to the lubricant to prevent oxidation and the formation of acids which cause corrosion.

Temperature Control

The force used to overcome friction appears as heat which, if not controlled, will cause high bearing temperatures. The lubricant reduces the heat produced by reducing friction and, in addition, may be used to carry off heat from the bearing surfaces. In the latter case, a common arrangement is to circulate generous quantities of the lubricant to the bearing where it picks up heat. The lubricant is then cooled in a heat exchanger before returning to the bearing again.

Shock Absorption

In cases where surfaces come together with some impact, as with gear teeth intermeshing, the lubricant serves to absorb shock.

Sealing

Lubricants are frequently used to provide sealing, such as between pistons and cylinder walls, or in rotating shaft seals.

CLASSES OF LUBRICANTS

Lubricants are manufactured to meet the requirements of the service for which they are intended. The particular properties desired will depend upon the nature of the surfaces to be lubricated, the load carried, the speed of rubbing, and the operating temperature.

Lubricants in general must provide the following services, with emphasis being placed upon one or more of these according to the needs of the particular application:

1. Minimum coefficient of friction.

2. Maximum adhesion to the surfaces to be lubricated.

3. Physical stability under variations of temperature and pressure.

4. Resistance to oxidation.

5. Resistance to emulsion (an emulsion is a liquid dispersal in a liquid).

6. Fluidity at low temperatures.

The great majority of lubricants are mineral oils, manufactured from crude petroleum oil; others are greases (which are a mixture of mineral oil and soap), animal, vegetable, and fish oils, synthetic oils, and solids.

Lubricants are divided into three general classes: solid, semi-solid, and liquid.

Solid Lubricants

Solid lubricants are suitable for use under conditions of high load and/or extreme (high or low) temperatures. In addition, they are frequently used where the bearing is subjected to contact with materials, such as chemicals, which would have a deteriorating effect on other classes of lubricants.

Other applications are lubrication of idle equipment in storage, and lubrication of bearings that are difficult to service because of their locations. Solid lubricants are also used to lubricate electrical equipment and instruments where other classes of lubricants would collect dirt and become gummy.

Materials that are used as solid lubricants are graphite, soapstone, molybdenum disulphide, mica, and polymer films.

The solid lubricants are applied to the bearing surfaces in various ways. They may be applied directly by rubbing and polishing. Often they are dispersed in a liquid and distributed in this way. Another method is to mix the solid lubricant with a bonding agent in a solvent, then spray and bake the mixture onto the surface.

Semi-Solid Lubricants

Semi-solid lubricants or greases are produced by combining a liquid lubricant, usually petroleum oil, with a thickening agent.

The fact that grease has a thick or stiff constituency means that it will not usually leak form a bearing and leave it dry. Also, grease is less likely to drip or splash from bearings and it therefore finds wide application in the textile and food industries.

It is suitable for ball bearings and roller bearings and a single application of grease to the bearing housing will be sufficient for an extended period of time. As well as lubricating, grease seals a bearing from dirt and water and gives the working surfaces a permanent protective coating that does not drain away to allow rusting during idle periods. The equipment needed for grease lubrication is less expensive and less complicated than for a liquid lubricant. Grease is also more convenient in handling and replenishment and requires much less frequent attention.

Grease is not suitable, however, where large amounts of heat must be continually carried away from the bearing and under these conditions a liquid lubricant would be used.

The characteristics required of an effective grease are purity, consistency, chemical stability, thermal stability, and tenacity. These are largely determined by the thickening agent or "soap" used in manufacture of a grease.

1. Calcium (Lime) Base Greases

The calcium or lime greases are the cheapest in cost and are the most commonly used. They are used for cup grease, pressure gun grease, axle grease, and water pump grease.

They are not suitable for use where temperatures exceed 71°C, as above this temperature the grease will lose its moisture and the soap and the oil will separate. They are insoluble in water and can therefore be used under damp conditions.

2. Sodium (Soda) Base Greases

The sodium base greases are more adhesive and cohesive than are the calcium base greases. Also, they are suitable for temperatures as high as 120°C. However, they are soluble in water and therefore are not suitable for wet conditions. They are frequently used for high speed ball and roller bearings.

3. Mixed Base Greases

These have a mixture of sodium and calcium for their base. They are water resistant to some degree and can withstand higher temperatures than the calcium base types.

4. Barium and Lithium Base Greases

These are greases, which use either barium or lithium as a base. They are water resistant and are suitable for high temperature service. They find use in antifriction bearings (roller and ball bearings). Some types of lithium base greases are suitable for extreme low temperatures (-50°C).

5. Aluminum Base Greases

These types have good water resistance and may be used for temperatures up to 82°C. They are very adhesive and stick well to metal surfaces thus providing rust protection. This adhesiveness or stickiness makes them unsuitable for high speed applications as they have excessive internal friction.

6. Specialty Greases

These are composed of mineral oils which have been thickened with solid lubricants such as graphite, mica, and talc. They are used for heavily loaded machinery operating at slow speeds such as tractor rollers, cement mixers, and excavating equipment.

Liquid Lubricants

Liquid lubricants are divided into three general classes: mineral oils, fixed oils, and synthetic oils.

1. Mineral Oils

Mineral oils are produced from crude petroleum and are the most commonly used class. The crude petroleum, from which gasoline, kerosene, and light fuel oil have already been extracted, is processed in a fractionating tower and the various grades of lubricating oil are drawn off at different levels from the tower. The heavy oils are drawn off near the bottom of the tower while the lighter grades of oil are removed from the higher levels of the tower.

2. Fixed Oils

Fixed oils, which are also called fatty oils, are of animal or vegetable origin and include lard, whale oil, castor oil, cottonseed oil, and rapeseed oil. These are rarely used by themselves as lubricants but are incorporated into greases or mixed with mineral oils for special applications.

3. Synthetic Oils

This class includes polyglycols and silicones. They are suitable for high temperature service and some types are used as fire resistant turbine lubricants.

Other desirable properties are resistant to sludge formation and oxidation. Synthetic oils are very expensive with some costing around $100 per litre.

LUBRICATING OIL PROPERTIES

Viscosity

Viscosity is a measure of the resistance of a liquid to internal deformation or shear. It indicates the liquid's ability to flow and, in the case of a lubricating oil, the viscosity determines the ability of the oil to support a load, the power required to overcome internal friction, and the amount of heat that will be produced due to internal friction.

The viscosity of an oil is greatly affected by the temperature of the oil. As the temperature increases, the oil will thin out and become less viscous (viscosity will be reduced). Conversely, at low temperatures, the oil will be thicker and more viscous (viscosity will be increased).

A commonly used method of measuring the viscosity of an oil is by means of a Saybolt viscosimeter. With this instrument, the time taken for a given quantity of oil at a given temperature to flow through a small diameter tube is measured in seconds. This viscosity is expressed in units called "Saybolt Seconds Universal" (SSU).

Viscosity Index

This viscosity index is a measurement of how much the viscosity of an oil changes with a change in temperature. A high viscosity index (V.I.) indicates that the oil's viscosity changes little with temperature change.

Oils with a very high V.I. are favoured for use in automatic transmissions in automobiles and other applications where temperature is likely to change, either seasonally or due to operating conditions.. This is because the oil will have a suitable viscosity at operating temperatures and still will not be too thick or viscous at lower temperatures, such as during a cold start-up.

Pour Point

The pour point of an oil is the lowest temperature at which the oil will flow. Oils that are used in cold climates or as refrigeration oils must have low pour points, otherwise they may congeal in service and lubrication flow will fail.

Flash and Fire Points

The flash point of an oil is the temperature at which the oil will give off sufficient vapour to ignite momentarily when mixed with air and exposed to a source of ignition.

The fire point of an oil is the temperature at which enough vapour is given off to burn continuously.

Flash and fire points are important as they indicate the temperature at which a fire or explosion may occur when temperature rises during operating conditions.

Neutralization Number

The neutralization number indicates the acidity of an oil. When lubricating oils are in service, they tend to oxidize and form acids. By testing an oil periodically it can be determined if its neutralization number has changed and this will give an indication of when the oil should be replaced.

Carbon Residue

The carbon residue test is used to determine the amount of carbon that an oil will form when subjected to high temperatures. The carbon residue factor is important in choosing a suitable oil for high temperature service, since carbon formation will interfere with the functioning of engine and compressor parts, such as piston rings and valves.

Floc Point

Floc point is the temperature at which the wax in the oil will separate out.

LUBRICATING OIL ADDITIVES

Frequently it is possible to improve the desirable characteristics of a lubricating oil by the use of additives. These are materials that are added to the oil and which improve certain characteristics of the oil without adversely affecting other characteristics. A large variety of these additives are in use, including the following.

Anti-oxidants: decrease the amount of oxygen that will react with the oil, thus preventing bearing corrosion and deposits of varnish and sludge.

Detergent-dispersants: keep deposit-forming substances in suspension in the oil so they can't settle out as deposits on bearing surfaces.

Viscosity index improvers: reduce the amount of viscosity change that an oil epxeriences with temperature changes.

Antifoam additives: cause the collapse of air or vapour bubbles that form within the oil and thus prevent the oil from foaming.

Pour point depressants: lower the pour point of the oil, thus allowing it to remain fluid at low temperatures.

Corrosion inhibitors: form a film on metal surfaces of a bearing, thus protecting them from contact with gases (particularly oxygen) and fluids that would cause corrosion.

SELECTION OF LUBRICATING OILS

The following sections deal with the various applications requiring lubricating oils and the desirable properties that the appropriate oil must possess.

Turbine Oils

The oil used in a turbine circulating system functions as both a lubricant and a cooling medium for the bearings. In addition, in many cases, the oil also serves as a sealing medium.

A turbine oil should be readily separated from water which may contaminate it, and should incorporate corrosion inhibitors, antifoam and anti-oxidant additives.

Consideration has been given in recent years to the use of synthetic fire resistant turbine oils. These will no doubt gain in popularity due to the fact that turbine lubricating oil lines are usually in close proximity to high temperature lines, with subsequent fire hazard should an oil leak develop.

Air Compressor Cylinder Oils

The viscosity must be within a suitable range at the operating temperatures of the compressor. If the viscosity is too high, then the oil will not spread rapidly over the cylinder walls and will cause a drag on the piston. Conversely, if the viscosity is too low, then the oil will not maintain the proper lubricating film or the proper sealing of piston rings.

In addition to having the proper viscosity, the oil should have a low carbon residue and, in cases where the compressor cylinder is lubricated by the splash method from the crankcase, the oil used would have to be suitable for both bearing and cylinder lubrication.

Internal Combustion Engine Oils

For internal combustion engine service, the oil is required to withstand the high temperature existing at the cylinder walls. When exposed to this high temperature, the oil will tend to evaporate and thicken and so form varnish and carbon deposits.

In addition to withstanding these high cylinder temperatures, the oil must lubricate the crankshaft and other bearings that are at a lower temperature, particularly at start-up.

A suitable engine oil will have a high viscosity index so that flow will be satisfactory at both the high operating temperatures and the low starting temperatures.

Additives usually include anti-oxidants, detergent dispersants, rust preventives and corrosion inhibitors.

Refrigeration Compressor Oil

The pour point must be low enough so that the oil will not congeal at evaporator temperatures and the oil must not react chemically with the refrigerant used. Some refrigerants, such as Freon, mix easily with oil, resulting in a reduction of the oil's viscosity. Therefore, a higher viscosity oil would be used in a Freon system than in an ammonia system.

Gear Lubricating Oils

For enclosed gears, such as turbine reduction gears, a low viscosity oil is preferred because it reduces power losses by reducing oil drag and it prevents excessive oil heating by reducing fluid friction. Extreme pressure additives are often incorporated in the oil to improve the load carrying ability.

For heavy industrial open gears, a high viscosity oil is used because it will cling to the surfaces and will resist washing off.

TYPES OF BEARING LUBRICATION

Lubrication can be divided, very generally speaking, into two categories: boundary lubrication and fluid film lubrication.

Boundary Lubrication

Boundary lubrication refers to lubrication where the surfaces are separated by only a microscopic film of the lubricant. This type of lubrication takes place when the supply of lubricant is restricted or intermittent. A certain amount of metal to metal contact will exist between the surfaces but, as the surfaces are wetted by the microscopic film, friction and wear will be reduced.

For slow speeds and heavy loads "oiliness" or film strength of the lubricant is an all-important factor. These conditions of operation indicate that a grease or a solid lubricant should be used. The greases provide greater wetting ability than conventional oil. Solid lubricants should be used only under special conditions.

Fluid Film Lubrication

Fluid film lubrication, also called flood lubrication, occurs when the lubricating film between surfaces is thick enough to completely separate the surfaces. This condition will exist only if the bearing clearance space is flooded with oil and if the moving surface in the bearing is in continual motion.

In the case of a turbine or engine main bearing, the rapidly revolving shaft will force oil underneath it and as a result, the shaft will float on a film of oil. The shaft must be rotating above a certain minimum speed in order to be able to force the oil beneath it. For this reason, most of the wear in a bearing will occur during stopping and starting periods when the shaft is rotating below the minimum speed and only boundary lubrication is in effect.

Fig. 2 illustrates how fluid film lubrication is established in a shaft bearing.

FIGURE 2

Fluid Film Formation in a Sleeve Bearing

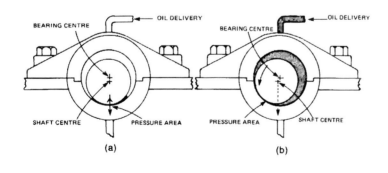

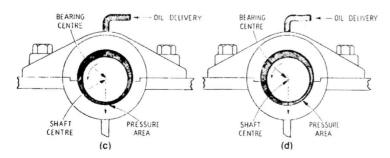

In Fig. 2(a) the shaft is not turning and is in contact with the bottom of the bearing. When the shaft begins to rotate in Fig. 2(b), it tends to roll up the side of the bearing and oil flows in behind and below it. As the shaft speed increases, Fig. 2(c), the oil is forced by the shaft into the wedge shaped space in front of and below the shaft and enough pressure is produced to separate the shaft from the bearing surface. At high speed, Fig. 2(d), the shaft is forced slightly over to the right due to the oil pressure.

At high speeds, the oil film separating the shaft from the bearing becomes thicker due to the increased pumping action of the shaft. As the speed decreases, the film thickness lessens until, at slow speeds, it breaks down and only boundary lubrication exists.

SHELL OR SLEEVE BEARINGS

The shell or sleeve bearing is usually constructed with a white-metal alloy lining carried on a cast iron or steel housing. The relatively soft, white-metal alloy is suitable for the lining because it will yield or deform slightly to conform to load conditions and is soft enough to allow foreign particles to become imbedded in it rather than score the shaft. Its comparative softness allows it to "wear in" to a smooth condition and it is fairly corrosion resistant.

To achieve full fluid lubrication, the bearing must provide sufficient clearance around the shaft and the oil must be supplied in the low-pressure area of the bearing.

Some of the methods of oil supply to the sleeve bearing are illustrated in Fig. 3.

FIGURE 3

Methods of Oil Supply to
a Sleeve Bearing

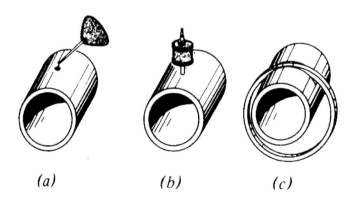

(a)   (b)   (c)

The simplest and oldest method of lubricating the bearing is the hand-operated oil can, Fig. 3(a). This method is only suitable for small bearings that require a few drops of oil every few weeks or months. Bearings on larger equipment need a steady oil supply. A feeding device such as the automatic oiler (wick-feed, gravity feed, etc.) gives a more continuous supply, Fig. 3(b), but the bearing may still run short of oil if the feeder is not refilled at regular intervals.

A more satisfactory method, common on pump and motor bearings, is the ring-oiled bearing shown in Fig. 3(c). The lower part of the bearing housing forms a reservoir, filled with oil. A ring rides on the shaft, through a slot in the center of the upper part of the bearing. When the shaft rotates, it moves the ring slowly and the ring picks up oil from the reservoir, drags it up through the bearing slot and from there it is distributed between the shaft and bearing. Once through the bearing, the oil drops back into the reservoir.

Oil Grooves in Bearings

Grooves are frequently employed in the top half of the bearing or non-pressure area for distributing the lubricant evenly ahead of the pressure area. Grooves in the actual pressure area are considered harmful because they tend to disrupt the oil film and reduce the size of this area.

Fig. 4 is a sketch of a sleeve bearing showing the point of oil supply and the point of greatest pressure.

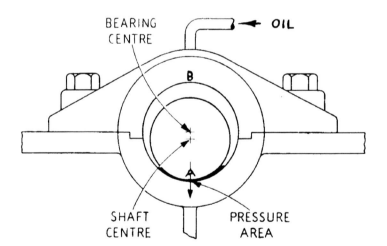

FIGURE 4

Sleeve Bearing Pressure Area

The ability of an oil film to lift and support a heavy load is dependent upon hydraulic pressure. This pressure is brought about by the pumping action of the rotating shaft, and any grooves in the pressure area will encourage metallic contact. Also, when bearings are composed of two or more parts fitted together, any sharp corners at the joints will tend to scrape the oil from the shaft. Therefore, all corners and edges should be chamfered or rounded to prevent this scraping action.

The principles of correct design and grooving of sleeve bearings may be summarized as follows:

1. Use grooves only where necessary for longitudinal distribution of the lubricant along the shaft (journal).

2. Do not cut grooves in the pressure area.

3. Chamfer or round off all sharp edges of bearing segments or grooves to prevent scraping the lubricant from the shaft.

4. To minimize end leakage, grooves and chamfers should extend only to within 1.25 cm or 0.5 inches of either bearing end.

5. Locate the lubricant application point in a portion of the bearing that is not under pressure.

6. Heavily loaded slow-speed bearings should have the lubricant application point closer to the pressure area than is required in higher-speed and more lightly loaded bearings.

Fig. 5 shows the location of oil groove and chamfer in a sleeve bearing.

FIGURE 5

Grooves and Chamfers
in Sleeve Bearing

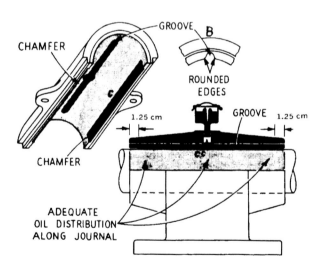

Bearing Failure

One of the first signs of a failing bearing is a rise in its operating temperature. Another sign is "knocking" or other unusual noises which indicate excessive wear.

Usually the cause of the bearing trouble is one or more of the following:

1. Improper viscosity of oil.

2. Improper bearing design (oil groove, chamfer, clearance).

3. Misalignment of shaft and bearing.

4. Loss of bearing metal due to corrosion or metal fatigue.

5. Loss of oil supply.

6. Temperature of oil too high.

Intolerable amounts of heat can be developed in bearings which are heavily loaded or if they support shafts which absorb heat from hot water, steam or other fluids to which they are exposed.

To prevent excessive temperatures, bearings are usually water cooled. This cooling takes place in one of the three following ways:

1. A special cooling water channel is cast in the bearing housing through which the water flows. This method is used for oil as well as grease lubricated bearings.

2. A special water coil is immersed in the oil basin of the bearing. The oil picks up the heat when it passes through the bearing and transfers it to the water passing through the coil.

3. Oil can be allowed to flow from the bearing reservoir and circulate through an oil cooler away from the bearing assembly before being recycled through the bearing for further lubrication and heat removal.

Emergency Cooling of a Hot Bearing

In the case of a small bearing, it is usually sufficient to increase the supply of oil, in this way increasing the rate of heat removal from the bearing.

Large bearings, however, are more difficult to cool. The heat produced may expand the shaft and thus reduce the clearance in the bearing. In this case, it may help to slacken off the bearing caps to increase the clearance. Frequently, the application of steam cylinder oil will aid in cooling the bearing and in extreme cases, graphite or white lead may be added with the cylinder oil. These latter substances help to smooth the bearing surface by filling in the hollows that may exist.

Water should never be applied directly to the bearing housing since it may cause sudden shrinkage or distortion. If water is to be used it should be applied to the shaft adjacent to the bearing and thus bring about a gradual cooling.

THRUST BEARINGS

The purpose of a thrust bearing is to prevent a rotating shaft from moving in an axial direction. A simple type of thrust bearing, known as a collar thrust, is shown in Fig. 6.

FIGURE 6

Collar-type Thrust Bearing

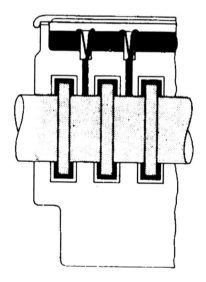

In this design, the collars, which are an integral part of the shaft, have their complete vertical surface areas pressing against the bearing surface and there is no room for an oil wedge to be formed. Lubrication is therefore of the boundary type and the load that this design can carry is limited.

A more suitable design has the bearing surfaces in the form of pads. These pads are free to tilt and thus allow the formation of an oil wedge to separate the bearing pad from the shaft collar.

Fig. 7 shows two types of tilting pad thrust bearings, the Michell in 7(a) and the Kingsbury in 7(b).

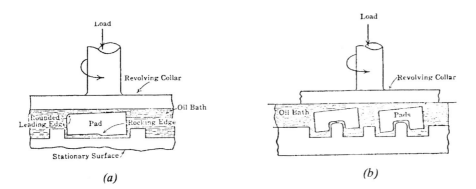

FIGURE 7

Schematic of Fluid Thrust Bearings

Fig. 8 shows more detail on the construction of a tilting-pad thrust bearing. In this design there are two sets of pads and thrust is prevented in both directions along the shaft.

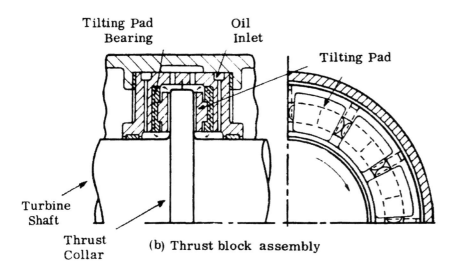

FIGURE 8

Tilting-Pad Thrust Bearing Arrangement

In the sleeve or shell bearings, the main purpose of the lubricant is to separate the surfaces by means of a lubricating film. This film may be microscopic in thickness as in the case of boundary lubrication, or it may be thick enough to float the shaft as in the case of fluid film lubrication.

BALL AND ROLLER BEARINGS

In the lubrication of ball and roller bearings the principle is somewhat different. In this type of bearing, also referred to as an **antifriction bearing**, the sliding of one surface over the other is largely replaced by a rolling motion, thereby largely eliminating surface friction. The main purposes of the lubricant in these bearings are:

1. To protect the accurately ground and highly polished surfaces of the balls, rollers, and raceways from corrosion. The smooth, low friction operation of these types of bearings depends to a large extent on the highly finished surfaces of the components. Therefore, if corrosion and consequent roughening of the surfaces occur, the bearing will fail rapidly.

2. To provide a seal to prevent the entrance of dirt or other impurities into the bearing housing.

3. To serve as a heat transfer medium to conduct away any heat generated at the contact points of rollers or balls.

4. To provide lubrication to reduce the small amount of sliding friction that is present even in the antifriction bearings.

Figure 9 shows one of many roller bearing designs and a simple oil feeder, the drop feed oiler. Notice the terminology used for the parts of the bearing. The inner "race" fits tightly on the shaft and turns with the shaft, while the outer "race" is held motionless in place by the bearing housing. Lubrication must be continuously provided to the rollers, which are turning at high speed between the races.

The oiler shown consists of an oil-filled cup that sits above the bearing housing and continuously drips oil down into the bearing. The operator must ensure that the cup is kept full to the operating level.

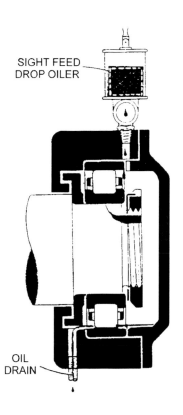

FIGURE 9

Roller Bearing and Oiler Designs

SIGHT FEED DROP OILER

OIL DRAIN

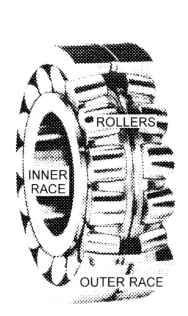

ROLLERS

INNER RACE

OUTER RACE

The lubricant used may be either oil or grease, depending upon operating conditions. In general, oil is preferred for the following conditions:

1. For light machines or instruments where resistance to rotation must be kept to a minimum.

2. Where speeds are high and the use of grease will produce excessive heating due to the work done in churning or displacing the grease.

3. For high operating temperatures. In some cases steam cylinder oil may be necessary.

4. Where bearings are located adjacent to other parts which require oil lubrication.

5. Where ambient temperatures are low.

In applications where speeds are not high and temperatures are not extreme, greases may be preferred for the following reasons:

1. Grease is less likely to be flung out or to leak from the bearings. This is an advantage in regard to keeping the adjacent surroundings clean.

2.   Where the atmosphere is polluted with impurities, grease provides a better seal to prevent entrance of these impurities into the bearing housing.

3.   Grease is more satisfactory for protecting bearings from corrosion during idle periods as it does not drain away as oil tends to do.

Ball and Roller Bearing Arrangements

The following figures show some typical roller and ball bearing arrangements, although there are many, many possible combinations. In Fig. 10 a cross-section of several designs is shown and it can be seen that ball and roller bearings can be used to provide both radial and axial (thrust) support.

FIGURE 10

Examples of Roller and Ball Bearing Designs

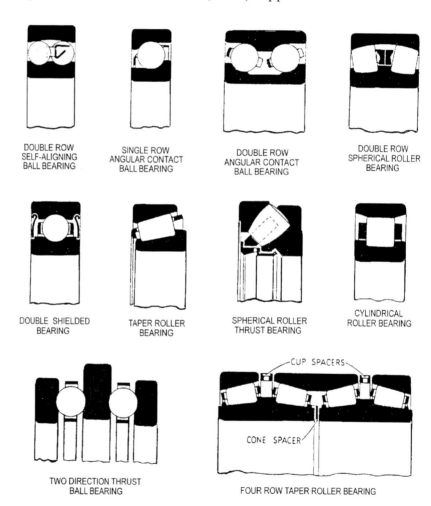

In Fig. 11 two ends of a shaft are represented. Here the ball bearing acts as a thrust bearing, taking care of axial loading on the shaft, and also the radial loading on the left end. The roller bearing handles radial loading at the right end of the shaft. Lubrication shown is grease, indicating a slow speed operation, but oil could also be fed to these bearings for higher speeds.

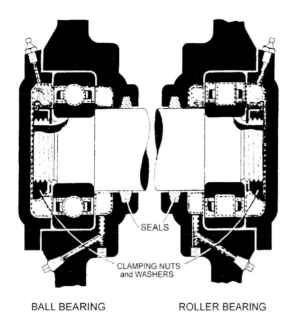

FIGURE 11

Typical Ball and Roller Bearing Installations

Fig. 12 shows a combination of roller and thrust bearings where the left end of the shaft is supported by a roller bearing and the right end has both a roller and a ball bearing. Again, the ball bearing handles any axial thrust and the roller bearing handles radial loading. This is common where fairly heavy bearing loads exist. The lubrication shown is forced oil feed, which enters at the top of the bearing casings and exits at the bottom, with a continuous flow maintained through the housings.

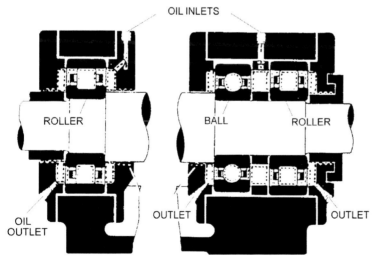

FIGURE 13

Typical Ball and Roller Bearing Combinations

Bearing Seals

To prevent foreign matter (dust, grit, water, etc) from entering the bearing housing, which would result in contamination of the lubricant, and to prevent the lubricant from leaking out of the housing, seals are installed on the shaft where it enters the bearing housing. These seals consist of felt, synthetic rubber, or leather rings, enclosed by their own steel casing and sometimes fitted with a light spring to force the seal against the shaft, Fig. 13.

FIGURE 13

Examples of Bearing Seals

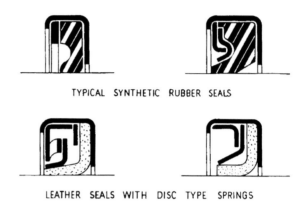

TYPICAL SYNTHETIC RUBBER SEALS

LEATHER SEALS WITH DISC TYPE SPRINGS

Fig. 14 shows a seal mounted in the housing of a ball bearing that may be either oil or grease lubricated.

FIGURE 14

Seal Mounted to Ball Bearing Housing

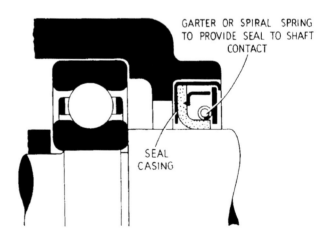

GARTER OR SPIRAL SPRING TO PROVIDE SEAL TO SHAFT CONTACT

SEAL CASING

Applying Grease Lubricants

When grease is used as the lubricant for ball or roller bearings, the bearing housing should not be filled more than one-third full. More than this will result in excessive drag or fluid friction, which will produce overheating. Care must be taken to ensure that dirt does not enter the bearing when applying the grease and the softest grease suitable for the particular service should be used.

Causes of Antifriction Bearing Failure

Ball and roller bearings, even when properly maintained and lubricated, will eventually fail due to metal fatigue. However, certain detrimental operating conditions can cause premature bearing failure, and some of these conditions are discussed below.

1. Poor Quality Lubricant

If the lubricant, such as a grease, forms a hard mass within the bearing, then the rollers or balls will not be free to move and the bearing will wear. Also, hard pieces of lubricant will be pressed into the bearing surfaces which will produce flaking and pitting.

2. Improper Fitting

If, when pressing a bearing into place on a shaft, the force is applied through the balls or rollers, then the surface under the balls or rollers will be indented or nicked. This condition is known as **brinelling** and will cause eventual bearing failure.

An improper fitting procedure will also cause cracking or splitting of the bearing race. This may be due to forcing the bearing onto a shaft that is too large. It may also be due to the force not being applied squarely to the race during installation.

3. Misalignment

Misalignment of a shaft, such as due to a driving belt that is too tight, will cause uneven loading of the bearing, resulting in surface flaking and excessive wear.

4. False Brinelling

This occurs in stationary bearings that are subjected to vibration. It resembles true brinelling as described in the section on improper fitting in that it produces indentations in the surfaces in contact with the balls or rollers.

5. High Operating Temperatures

Usually, the bearing can withstand operating temperatures up to 120°C (250°F). Above this, however, the metal tends to soften and excessive wear will result. For this reason it is advisable to control bearing temperatures to the manufacturer's recommendations when possible. The generally accepted maximums are in the range of 65°C to 70°C (150°F to 160°F) unless otherwise stated.

FORCED-FEED LUBRICATION SYSTEMS

Forced-feed lubrication systems supply oil, under pressure and continuous flow to the bearings of rotating equipment. This system is very common on steam and gas turbines and large pumps where lubrication control is critical in terms of flow, temperature and cleanliness. In most cases there is an external "lube oil skid" that delivers the oil, at controlled pressure and temperature, to the equipment and then receives the return flow.

Figure 15 shows the typical components of a lube oil skid.

FIGURE 15

Components of a Lube
Oil Skid

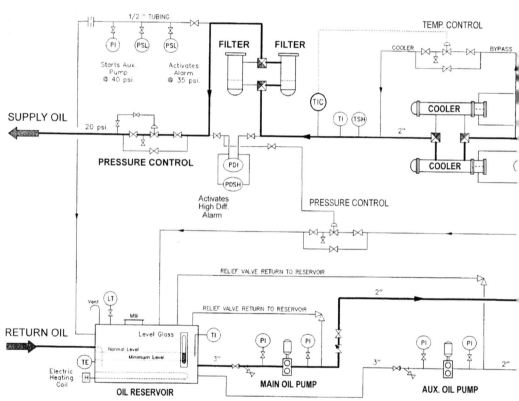

Supply and return flows center around a reservoir in which a minimum oil level is maintained. A main oil pump, usually positive displacement type, draws from the reservoir and delivers the oil under pressure to the supply line of the equipment bearings, etc. The oil passes through a set of coolers with an automatic bypass that controls the downstream temperature. Typical cooling mediums are water/glycol (in a shell-and-tube exchanger) and air (in a fin-fan cooler).

Next the oil if filtered, via a duplex filter system in which one filter is always on standby and flow can be switched, for filter cleaning, without disrupting flow. Note that the pressure differential across the filters is continuously monitored, to warn of flow restriction. The oil pressures in the system are controlled by a recirculation line on the pump discharge and by a pressure reducing station at the entrance to the supply line.

The auxiliary oil pump is a standby that will start automatically if oil pressure drops below a certain minimum.

Fig. 16 shows the supply and return at a turbine and pump arrangement. Quite often the oil reservoir will be directly below the turbine and the major oil components, such as pumps, cooler, filters will be mounted directly to the turbine base framework. Also, the oil system may supply oil to the turbine's governor system and the turbine may have a built-in oil pump that draws suction from the reservoir and acts as the main oil pump.

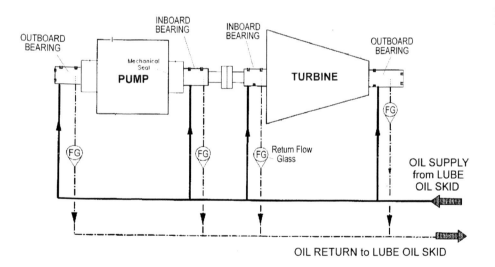

FIGURE 16

Simple Oil Supply and Return from Turbine and Pump

Fig. 17 shows a very simplified version of the lube oil system for a small gas turbine. Here the main oil pump is driven directly by the turbine, so only delivers oil when the turbine itself is rotating. A second, electric pump is used on turbine start-up until the unit is up to speed, and on shutdown, to maintain oil circulation as the turbine slows down. Note that the system also supplies oil to the speed-reducing gear. Two sets of filters are used and the oil cooler, in this case, is a fin-fan type.

FIGURE 17

Simplified Oil System for
a Gas Turbine

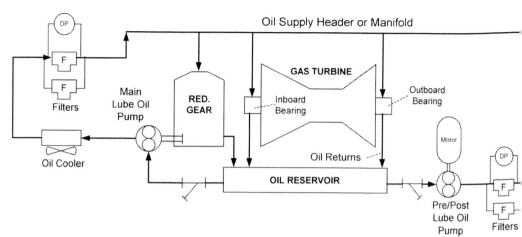